# How to Prepare for Interviews and Develop Your Career

## As a Nurse or Midwife

*This book is dedicated to all health and social care staff and students, who deserve structured support and clinical supervision throughout their career, respect for the daily challenges they face and a commitment from government to improve staffing levels across services.*

# How to Prepare for Interviews and Develop Your Career

## As a Nurse or Midwife

**CAROL FORDE-JOHNSTON**

RGN, BSc (Hons), PGDip, RNT, MSc

Divisional Recruitment and Retention Lead
Oxford University Hospitals NHS Foundation Trust

Lantern

**ISBN 9781908625830**

First published in 2020 by Lantern Publishing Ltd

Lantern Publishing Ltd, The Old Hayloft, Vantage Business Park, Bloxham Rd, Banbury
OX16 9UX, UK

**www.lanternpublishing.com**

**British Library Cataloguing in Publication Data**
A catalogue record for this book is available from the British Library

The authors and publisher have made every attempt to ensure the content of this book
is up to date and accurate. However, healthcare knowledge and information is changing
all the time so the reader is advised to double-check any information in this text on drug
usage, treatment procedures, the use of equipment, etc. to confirm that it complies with
the latest safety recommendations, standards of practice and legislation, as well as local
Trust policies and procedures. Students are advised to check with their tutor and/or
practice supervisor before carrying out any of the procedures in this textbook.

Typeset by Medlar Publishing Solutions Pvt Ltd, India
Cover design by AM Design
Printed in the UK
Last digit is the print number: 10  9  8  7  6  5  4  3

# CONTENTS

**STEP 7**
MAKE YOUR ACHIEVEMENTS STAND OUT
IN THE FUTURE

# ABOUT THE AUTHOR

**Carol Forde-Johnston** (RGN, BSc (Hons), PGDip, RNT and MSc) is a Divisional Recruitment and Retention Lead in the Oxford University Hospitals NHS Foundation Trust. Her current role involves leading recruitment and retention initiatives and providing structured career advice to all levels of staff, with a particular focus on supporting newly qualified nurses and international nurses. Carol qualified as a registered nurse in 1989 at Coventry School of Nursing and went on to specialise in neurosciences, working her way up to G grade nursing sister. She worked for 20 years as a lecturer practitioner, a joint appointment between Oxford Brookes University and the local NHS hospital Trust, enabling her to integrate research, education and clinical practice into her role. As a lecturer practitioner, Carol led a third year nursing degree module at Oxford Brookes University and supported nursing apprenticeships as part of her Trust role.

Carol has published numerous articles relating to education and practice development in UK and European nursing and medical journals. In 2015 she created and evaluated a *three-tiered curriculum Foundation Preceptorship programme* for all newly qualified nurses within the Oxford University Hospitals NHS Foundation Trust. The programme integrated skills development, theoretical study days and clinical supervision using action learning sets.

Carol has also been involved in several patient improvement initiatives and collaborated with Oxford University on a staff-led quality improvement project to prevent inpatient hospital falls. She is currently in her third year at Oxford Brookes University studying for a PhD in nursing and plans to conduct an observational study examining nurse–patient interactions at the bedside in hospital wards that use electronic patient records (EPR). Carol is passionate about developing and supporting staff and student nurses to improve their confidence and fulfil their future aspirations.

# PREFACE

The practical advice offered within this book has been developed from 20 years' experience as a lecturer practitioner, guiding the professional and academic development of pre-registration nursing students, newly qualified and experienced nurses. It is also based on over 30 years' experience working in clinical practice, recruiting staff and leading interview panels.

This book is a practical manual written for all nurses and midwives who require clear career advice to fulfil their aspirations. The contents are just as relevant to students preparing for their first post and preceptorship year as they are for newly qualified or senior staff needing to structure professional development plans and submit applications for higher banded posts or post-registration opportunities. Guidance and tips are organised under '7 key steps' that demonstrate how being prepared, proactive, systematic and able to access support, are key to positively developing your future career.

This book aims to help:
- students and registered nurses/midwives reviewing potential roles and career pathways aligned to professional and academic requirements
- students and registered nurses/midwives preparing application documents, CVs, personal statements or personal portfolios for jobs, post-registration courses, bursaries or internship/fellowship opportunities
- students and registered nurses/midwives preparing for an interview, which includes planning potential interview questions and structuring responses
- students and registered nurses/midwives developing a clinical academic career
- students and registered nurses/midwives aiming to influence practice in their current role through service improvement, research or clinical governance projects

- newly qualified or experienced registered nurses/midwives preparing learning and development plans for professional development reviews and appraisals, including NMC revalidations
- newly qualified or experienced registered nurses/midwives needing to access guidance and support to help them deal with challenges in the workplace
- university lecturers, clinical educators, practice supervisors and managers offering career advice to develop students and staff.

Nowadays, nurses and midwives have a variety of courses, roles and career pathways to navigate across the UK. However, not everyone knows which opportunity to go for, which role to apply for, which course to undertake or how to apply for funding and study leave. *Step 1* presents a range of roles and career pathways to help align your professional and academic development. Practical strategies presented in *Step 2* advise how to proactively lead your learning and development, and access local/national support networks. Post-qualification education and training courses are explained, along with guidance to assist applications for future funding.

Key managerial, leadership, communication and organisational skills can be demonstrated through your contribution to local service improvement, research and clinical governance projects, to influence positive change at work. *Step 3* invites you to consider how you can positively support others and influence change in your current role, to help your application, CV and personal portfolio stand out.

Competition inevitably increases as you move up the career ladder, as there are fewer band 6, 7 and 8 posts, in comparison to band 5 roles. Practical guidance to help you complete an application form, personal statement, CV and portfolio is clearly presented within *Step 4*. Simple tips and example personal statements are presented for individuals wishing to apply for their first post or for more experienced staff applying for course funding. Ultimately, the outcome of any competitive interview is down to your preparation and performance on the day. With methodical preparation, you are more likely to pre-empt interview questions and be able to handle spontaneous questions on the day. The practical advice offered in *Step 5* will help guide your interview preparation. Example interview questions are presented under common themes, which include clear advice on how to structure your answers.

It is difficult to thrive in your career and develop professionally if you are experiencing stress, conflict or a lack of support at work. You may feel just as out of depth starting a new course or a senior position, as you did when you were newly qualified. Within *Step 6*, an overview of national workforce pressures highlights the need for employers to take responsibility for supporting staff wellbeing in the workplace. Practical guidance covers areas such as: how to prevent and manage stress; how to resolve communication issues in the workplace; and how to access support to promote your wellbeing. A list of available support services and national frameworks to retain staff are also presented for you to access, or use to support others.

It is important that professionals share their achievements with others, to influence and inform practice and contribute to a professional evidence base. *Step 7* provides practical guidance and tips to disseminate and promote your work, through networking, collaborating with others and publishing. Advice on how to develop a clinical academic career is also presented; this involves working in clinical practice whilst undertaking academic study and research, to advance practice and transform care.

Future investment in clinical practice educator posts, and structured preceptorship, clinical supervision and staff wellbeing programmes, are vital to retain nurses and midwives in the future. It is hoped that the practical guidance offered within this book will help to inform your professional and academic development and enable you to receive the support you deserve in the future, to positively progress your career.

*Carol Forde-Johnston*

# ACKNOWLEDGEMENTS

Firstly, I would like to thank publishing director Peter Oates and the staff at Lantern Publishing for supporting the release of my second book; you are all amazing at what you do. My publishing career would never have started if you hadn't seen potential in one of my journal articles, Peter, and I will be forever grateful.

Massive thanks to my husband, James, and 9-year-old daughter Clodagh, for just getting on with it and not complaining when I spent so many weekends this last year hunched over a computer. I love you both more than words can say; marrying a man who can cook better than me was the best decision of my life!

Finally, thanks to my parents, Clare and Jim, my sister Sharon and mother-in-law Kath for your continual love, encouragement and babysitting. I couldn't have done it without you and I am blessed to have you in my life.

# ABBREVIATIONS

| | | | |
|---|---|---|---|
| AHP | allied health professional | MDT | multidisciplinary team |
| APEL | Accreditation of Prior Experiential Learning | MSW | maternity support worker |
| CCG | clinical commissioning group | NHS | National Health Service |
| | | NHSI | NHS Improvement |
| CN | charge nurse | NICE | National Institute for Health and Care Excellence |
| CPD | continuous practice development | | |
| CQC | Care Quality Commission | NIHR | National Institute for Health Research |
| CV | curriculum vitae | | |
| DBS | Disclosure and Barring Service | NMC | Nursing and Midwifery Council |
| EBP | evidence-based practice | NQM | newly qualified midwife |
| EPR | electronic patient records | NQN | newly qualified nurse |
| H&SC | Health and Social Care | NRLS | National Reporting and Learning System |
| HEE | Health Education England | | |
| | | NVQ | National Vocational Qualification |
| HEI | higher education institution | | |
| | | PALS | Patient Advice and Liaison Service |
| HQIP | Healthcare Quality Improvement Programme | | |
| | | PCC | person-centred community |
| HR | Human Resources | PDR | professional development review |
| HRA | Health Research Authority | | |
| | | PHE | Public Health England |
| IV | intravenous | PIP | performance improvement plan |
| KPI | key performance indicator | | |

| | | | |
|---|---|---|---|
| QAA | The Quality Assurance Agency for Higher Education | RN | registered nurse |
| RCM | Royal College of Midwives | SMART | Specific, Measurable, Achievable, Realistic, Time-based |
| RCN | Royal College of Nursing | UCAS | Universities and Colleges Admissions Service |
| RM | registered midwife | VBI | values-based interview |
| | | WTE | whole time equivalent |

# STEP 1

# KNOW YOUR CAREER OPTIONS AND WHAT YOU NEED TO GET THERE

*"By faithfully working eight hours a day you may eventually get to be boss and work twelve hours a day."*
Robert Frost (1874–1963), American poet

## 1.1 THE IMPORTANCE OF CHOOSING THE RIGHT JOB AND CAREER PATHWAY

From my observations over the last 30 years, nurses and midwives who have successful careers and are content at work have often proactively aligned their qualifications and experiences to a job that suits their strengths and passions. They will usually listen to, and act on, constructive feedback from others, recognising where their abilities lie. Alternatively, they may luckily have found themselves supported in a role where this alignment just happens to fall into place.

By contrast, finding yourself unhappy in a role, working in a demotivating team, being overlooked for seconded educational courses or frustrated as you have remained at the same banding for years, can be soul destroying. You will spend approximately a third of your life at work, so finding a job and developing a career that fulfils your needs and aspirations will contribute to your own health and wellbeing and help you to support and care for others. There is a lack of research examining the impact of professional development and academic support on the retention and career progression of nurses and midwives in the UK. Future workforce studies need to focus on this area to encourage individuals to join our profession and prevent registered staff leaving.

This chapter, which describes the first step on your road to a fulfilling career, aims to help you move your career forward positively by identifying a role/career pathway to suit your needs. You will find the tips throughout this chapter helpful, whether you are a:

- third year student nurse/midwife planning your first role
- newly qualified registered nurse (NQN)/midwife (NQM) or experienced registered nurse (RN)/registered midwife (RM) planning to move up a band
- RN/RM contemplating a sideways career move
- senior nurse/midwife, educator or manager guiding junior staff.

### 1.1.1 Do your groundwork and prepare

I have spent over 30 years guiding students, registered and non-registered nurses with their career development, which has included preparing all bands of staff for interviews. I am continuously surprised by the number of staff who have little idea what they need to do to progress their career or how much preparation is required to get there. Career development is not just about going up the bands either, as research and educational opportunities may arise in your current role that you are keen to apply for.

Unfortunately the realisation that someone has not prepared thoroughly hits them when they are rejected at the shortlisting stage, or receive interview feedback stating that their answers were not *'in-depth enough'*, they did not *'have as many skills as the other candidate'* or the classic *'you did not sell yourself enough'*. It is disheartening when colleagues feed back that they could not answer questions in their interview, when a little more preparation might have resulted in a successful outcome.

Preparation and planning are also important for longer-term career development and not just for interviews. RNs/RMs may feel unfulfilled in their current role, as it does not meet their expectations, or they simply outgrow their banding and want more job satisfaction. The worst case scenario is to realise that the perfect role or training course is about to be advertised but you do not have the academic or professional qualifications to apply. This is even more upsetting if your employer previously gave you the opportunity to complete the qualification but you decided not to take up the offer and further funding has been withdrawn. Nursing and midwifery educational budgets are determined annually and, in turn, can increase or decrease yearly (see *Step 2*).

In summary, understanding what a particular role or career pathway entails, what opportunities are available to you to develop, and the preparation required to take advantage of them, is essential to improve your chances of success. More importantly, you are more likely to be happy in your chosen career if you understand key aspects of the role you are striving towards. All of which leads to the first step in this book: know your career options and what is required to get there!

### 1.1.2 Expectation versus reality: is this really what you want to do?

The Robert Frost quote at the beginning of this chapter alludes to the importance of understanding what a particular role, career pathway or course actually involves, as the reality may be far from what you anticipate. An RN/RM may naively presume that because they have been working in an area for two years, they will easily walk through an in-house specialist course interview and be offered a training place, which is not always the case. When applying for any course place that requires funding and study leave, you need to ensure that you have manager support, your personal statement is of a high standard and you apply in time. During your interview, the interviewers will establish whether you have the academic ability required to meet the course requirements, along with being able to maintain a work–life balance whilst studying. Serious thought should be given to whether you can commit to the hours and self-directed study the course requires. Receiving highly sought-after paid study leave to complete any university accredited course is usually competitive, and interviews require rigorous preparation to avoid disappointment (see *Steps 4* and *5*).

Following registration, it is important to plan your progression and have a good understanding of what your next role or academic course will entail. Moving up a career ladder to become a band 7 manager, for example, can be rewarding and involves leading a team to make a difference for patients and staff. I worked for three years as a G grade nursing sister and loved it; however, it takes dedication, hard work and proactive career development to achieve this goal.

Today, many nursing and midwifery managers have to manage million-pound budgets that fund staffing and clinical resources. Due to increasing organisational responsibilities, we now have finance teams across healthcare services to support managers' decision-making and managers are encouraged to complete master's level management and leadership courses. A manager will only thrive in post if they are supported by their line manager to develop their core leadership skills. If you plan to become a manager in the future, you should take account of the organisational aspects of the role, and align relevant professional leadership experience and master's level study.

The same advice is relevant for any job or career trajectory you are planning, be it your first post as a registered practitioner, first move to a higher banding or a move to an alternative field of health care.

> ☰ **KEY TIPS**
>
> - To avoid disappointment it is important to understand fully what a job, course or career pathway actually entails before deciding to move your career forward.
> - Find out if it is really right for you!

## 1.2 HOW TO CHOOSE THE RIGHT CAREER PATHWAY

When I am discussing career pathways with staff or students, they sometimes ask me: *"How did you know which direction to take in nursing?"* or *"What made you want to become a Lecturer Practitioner?"* When I discuss my career journey they are often surprised:

*Number 1:* I didn't work hard at school or during my nursing course, I walked out of my A levels, and my Mum finally dragged me out of bed one morning and told me that I had to get a job. I was going to be a nurse like my Auntie as it would provide me with a regular wage. In the 1980s nursing jobs were scarce. During my nurse training I ended up being the only person in my cohort who failed their nursing finals, as I totally misread one of three final exam questions *(I understand how it feels to fail a module!)*.

*Number 2:* I initially had no idea where my career would take me and out of necessity took the first job I was offered on a neuroscience ward, as *'neuro'* was the only placement I really enjoyed during my training. None of the roles or courses I have completed since has been easily acquired. I have dealt with several rejections along the way; for example, I applied for a team leader post at three different hospitals before finally being offered the role.

*Number 3:* I enjoy writing but I am not particularly clever and certainly was not driven to complete further qualifications or progress up a career ladder when I first started nursing. I fell into my first role out of necessity and circumstance. However, I have always worked hard and once I acquired an interest through excellent role models, I was off! I met an amazing lecturer practitioner (LP) who inspired me and allowed me to shadow her...it all made sense...my perfect role! I identified the exact qualifications I needed to become an LP and did everything possible to align my professional and academic development towards this goal.

You can see from my personal career journey that there were times when my career was erratic, led by luck and circumstance. Later ambition and drive kicked in to enable me to pursue my ideal role.

☰ **KEY TIPS**

- Career pathways change according to personal circumstances and needs, and no one pathway will suit everyone all the time.
- Remember, if you fail courses or are unsuccessful when applying for jobs, there will always be another chance or an alternative option!

### 1.2.1 *Mountain climb, slow amble, cross-country trek, potholing or retracing past steps?*

When I run career development sessions with groups of staff, I use the following list to discuss different career journeys that they may experience along the way:

- Mountain climb
- Slow amble
- Cross-country trek
- Potholing
- Retracing steps.

I find discussions helpful to increase individuals' self-awareness in relation to what they want to do in the future and how they plan to get there. None of the journeys on the above list are better than others and I have walked all these paths during my career!

It is important to remember that personality traits and personal circumstances will be reflected in the way you approach your development, which may change over time. Values may alter according to your life experiences and you may have to deal with difficulties that affect your career development, such as bereavement, divorce or illness. You may need to adapt your development plans and be kind to yourself, taking time out from your studies or withdrawing from an interview, if it places you under too much pressure.

Most individuals go through different stages in life and the same happens with careers. I have known friends who took years to become a ward manager, but were right to wait until they had built up experiences in several fields, to ensure they had chosen their ideal role. Others rushed to take a higher paid band early in their career, only to return to a lower band later on, as they realised that quality of life meant more to them. It is helpful to gain an awareness of your own personality traits and learning needs by discussing your development and learning styles with others, e.g. your line manager, preceptor, educators, colleagues, family and friends (see *Section 1.2.6*).

Remember, just because someone knows exactly which role they want, and you do not, does not mean that their approach is better. Conversely, there is nothing wrong with being ambitious and knowing exactly which role you want; just prepare as much as you can and go for it! Case examples are presented below to demonstrate a range of career trajectories.

## The mountain climber

Ambitious, driven, focused, knows exactly what they want and how to get there.

 **CASE EXAMPLE**

An NQN knows that they want to eventually become a band 7 specialist nurse in breast care, as they lost their mum to breast cancer. They have spent time with the breast care team, as a third year student nurse, and know exactly which post-registration qualifications are required for the role. They know which ward will support them with a related post-registration course and have already approached the oncology team, been interviewed for a band 5 post, and have a job waiting for them on a speciality surgical ward when they qualify.

## The slow ambler

Developing at a slower pace, finding their feet in a new role or getting used to their current situation, happy to be led by others and just see what happens for now.

 **CASE EXAMPLE**

A band 5 RN has worked in a hospital setting for two years, as the employer supported her degree apprenticeship. She has always wondered what working in the community would be like. Her line manager decides to leave and encourages her to make the move to community to try it out or *"she will never know if it was for her or not"*. She loves her RN role and does not want to be a band 6 or climb any further up a career ladder. After a few months thinking about it, she decides to make a *'sideways'* move. She has recently been appointed as a band 5 in the community and is taking time to orientate herself over the next few months. She is used to having a team of people on a ward and needs time to adjust to managing her caseload more autonomously in her new community staff nurse role.

## The cross-country trekker

Knows what their end goal is and wants to get there carefully and steadily, uses a long and consistent approach to develop their career.

 **CASE EXAMPLE**

A band 5 perioperative practitioner has worked in scrubs and anaesthetics over the last five years and aspires to become a band 6 senior perioperative practitioner. He has met with a local clinical educator and has mapped out a long-term plan to aid his development that involves taking on an active link role, shadowing a band 6 and 7 over the next three months, and starting anaesthetic, surgical and recovery practice university modules. Once he becomes a band 6 and has finished his degree he plans to complete a short in-house leadership course.

## The potholer

Exploring exciting new challenges, taking the opportunity to see or do things that other staff have not done yet, pioneering new ways of practice.

 **CASE EXAMPLE**

A band 6 has worked on a mental health inpatient ward for the last year and she also volunteers in a local prison. The prison warden is so impressed with the way she supports inmates that he offers her a secondment as a band 6 for a year to pilot a new forensic mental health community model. She takes up the one-year secondment as the first band 6 to work in the prison with a small number of individuals who have offending histories and a range of mental health problems. These individuals have complex needs including homelessness, substance misuse and social exclusion. The warden is very impressed with the way she has performed in her role over the last year. At the end of her secondment, she is offered a full-time position with a view to setting up a new support service. The role will involve collaborating on a research project with a national charity for the homeless, the first of its kind in the country.

## The step retracer

Been there, done that! Wanting to go back to what they know best and enjoy most, happy to return to a past role for a better quality of life or less stress.

> 📂 **CASE EXAMPLE**
>
> A community midwifery manager has worked 35 years in his profession, the last 10 years as a band 8. His mother's Alzheimer's has recently worsened and his father is finding it difficult to cope alone. His daughter's husband has also recently lost his job and he wants to support his family as much as he can. He is finding the Matron role increasingly stressful, whilst trying to balance his home life. He would like to reduce his hours and go back to a band 6 for a few years before retiring, to focus on his family and have a better work–life balance.

### 1.2.2 Think about your future journey

Take some time thinking about which type of career journey you would like, what suits your current work–life balance and how you plan to move your career forward. Answering some of the following questions may help to focus your thoughts:

- Which of the career journeys above most reflects how you are developing now? *(If none of them reflects how you feel, then make up another journey)*
- What are your strengths and weaknesses?
- What motivates and interests you?
- Where do you see yourself in one year?
  - How do you plan to get there?
- Where do you see yourself in five years?
  - How do you plan to get there?
- Who can help guide your career development in your place of work now?

You will find additional pointers in the next section that may help guide your answers, such as discussing your development with an experienced member of staff or as part of an appraisal with your line manager.

### 1.2.3 What is out there and where can I go?

Across the UK the majority of nurses (79.2%) and nursing assistants (69.7%) work for the NHS, as opposed to the private or independent sector (Health and Social Care Information Centre, 2018). If you work for the NHS you will receive the benefits of working for the biggest employer in Europe and one of the most respected organisations. You will be eligible for the NHS pension scheme, which offers the most generous pension in Europe, along with the most flexible benefit packages. Healthcare students are most commonly trained in the NHS; however, there are alternative job opportunities and career pathways outside the NHS. You may wish to consider the advantages and disadvantages of working for different employers (see *Table 1.1*).

*Table 1.1: Alternative job opportunities*

| Careers on offer | Advantages | Disadvantages |
|---|---|---|
| Working for an agency | • You can continue in your present job and supplement your income or choose to work solely for an agency<br>• Choice of hours that you want to work, e.g. avoiding nights<br>• Choice of areas you want to work in, and being able to avoid those you don't<br>• Wages per hour may be higher than a permanent role<br>• Reduces the chance of burnout from working in the same job | • Work may not always be available in the areas you want<br>• If you do not work, you do not get paid (no paid sick days or holidays)<br>• Working across different sites in unfamiliar areas may be stressful<br>• Lack of consistency, if you do not book shifts in the same area<br>• Agencies usually offer no additional benefits, e.g. maternity leave<br>• Permanent staff are sometimes reluctant to work with agency staff<br>• Needing to keep receipts for tax purposes |
| Working abroad | • Travelling and living in other countries<br>• Experiencing different cultures and increasing cultural awareness<br>• Receiving large bonuses and pay incentives in some countries; e.g. Dubai does not impose any tax on personal salaries, and if you have worked for more than 2 years you will receive a lump sum of 15% of your annual salary on departure<br>• Enhancing your CV with improved communication/language skills<br>• Developing independence and transferable skills<br>• Housing costs and travel expenses may be paid as part of a package | • Work patterns, language and culture may be different and you may suffer 'culture shock'<br>• You may not be able to drive straight away in some countries<br>• Risk of loneliness without family and friends<br>• Some agencies charge you large amounts of fees and do not provide travel expenses/relocation costs<br>• You may need to pay for exams and courses to be eligible to work<br>• You may require expensive health insurance<br>• Learning a new language may prove difficult in a short space of time<br>• Not every country provides good working conditions |
| Working in the military | • Competitive pay, pension and career frameworks, e.g. following 2 years post-registration experience in acute care you will start on nursing officer pay<br>• World-class professional training given free<br>• Military will pay for individuals' Adult Nursing and Mental Health pre-registration degree<br>• Travelling and living in other countries as part of a military community<br>• National respect when caring for injured personnel and trauma victims | • You may be posted anywhere in the world including military bases, hospitals, clinics, overseas war zones or ships at sea<br>• You may be away from your family for months at a time<br>• Possibility of working in a combat zone |

*Table 1.1: (continued)*

| Careers on offer | Advantages | Disadvantages |
|---|---|---|
| Working for a private company | • Reduced caseload as private institutions generally see fewer patients<br>• Less burnout than seen in the public sector<br>• Pay and benefits will vary, depending on your employer, and may be higher, or lower, than the NHS<br>• You may receive perks such as regular health screenings, private health insurance, life insurance and free meals, depending on the company<br>• You may be offered more paid training opportunities than in the public sector | • You will not be part of the NHS pension scheme, which is the most generous pension scheme in Europe<br>• Independent employers do not have a national agreement in terms of salary, and you may need to negotiate the best deal for you *(always check the small print linked to pay increments and annual leave)*<br>• The independent sector is less likely to have defined career pathways in contrast to the structured 'banding' levels in the NHS<br>• Private institutions can go bankrupt, in which case you will be out of a job |
| Working for voluntary services | • Contributing to society is a rewarding experience<br>• Meeting new people and gaining skills to enhance your CV<br>• Increases your social network<br>• Personal growth | • You are not paid for your work and you may find allocating time to volunteer difficult, depending on your personal and social circumstances |

### 1.2.4 Range of fields and settings

When you train on a pre-registration nursing degree course, you usually choose to study one of four fields:
• Adult
• Children's (paediatrics)
• Learning disabilities
• Mental health.

Interestingly, we now have more universities offering dual training and the flexibility to move across specialities, e.g. four-year dual degrees in adult nursing and mental health; adult and children's nursing; or learning disability and child health. It is also worth noting that, following registration, any RN or RM may work within the field of neonatal care. Neonatal services usually offer band 5s comprehensive orientations over 3–6 months.

After qualifying in one field (or dual fields), there are more specialised roles you can undertake following the completion of a degree-level specialist practitioner programme, such as:
• district nurse
• health visitor

- general practice nurse
- neonatal nurse
- prison nurse
- school nurse.

On a pre-registration midwifery degree course, you are educated and trained to deliver care and provide health education to support mothers, newborn babies and families throughout the childbearing process. Health education aims to promote healthy family life, pregnancies and positive parenting, when working with women who are:
- pregnant (antenatal)
- labouring
- postnatal (postpartum).

The field of midwifery also offers an 18-month postgraduate course for adult nurses who have completed a bachelor nursing degree and wish to receive a dual qualification in adult nursing and midwifery.

Whatever your chosen field, you will have a variety of settings in which to work when you qualify, which include:
- hospital wards or clinics
- intensive care/high dependency units
- community settings
- schools
- GP practices
- nursing homes
- prisons
- hospices
- patients' homes.

### 1.2.5  More choice requires sound career advice

It is evident that we currently have staffing shortages across our health and social care services and employers are struggling to recruit and retain nurses and midwives. The promotion of structured career pathways and continuing professional development is vital to support our future workforce (see *Section 6.1* for a current overview of national workforce pressures and statistics).

Once qualified, an RN/RM will have a diverse range of roles and courses to apply for within the areas of clinical and advanced nursing practice, education and research (see *Tables 1.2–1.5* for a range of jobs and career pathways). A role in nursing or midwifery education, for example, may range from one-to-one teaching at the bedside or leading corporate training programmes for newly qualified staff, to running small groups to develop individuals' clinical skills, or presenting to 200 staff in a lecture theatre.

Due to the vast range of roles and career pathways available to you, it is especially important that you receive sound, positive and constructive career advice to aid your progression. I have supported nurses who were fantastic role models for newly qualified nurses at the bedside; however, they had initially discounted a career as a clinical educator, as they feared presenting to larger groups, or someone told them they were too quiet to teach other staff. It turns out clinical education was their ideal role, and once in post they were encouraged to develop their confidence by completing a teaching certificate; they can now present to larger groups too!

Strategies to help you choose a role or career pathway that suits your personal needs are presented in *Table 1.2*. Several national bodies also provide online resources to keep you up to date with career developments and opportunities, such as:

- Health Education England (HEE) *Health Careers*: www.hee.nhs.uk/our-work/health-careers
- NHS Scotland *Careers*: www.careers.nhs.scot
- NHS Wales *Careers*: www.wales.nhs.uk/nhswalesaboutus/workingfornhswales/careers
- NI Direct *Careers in Health and Social Care*: www.nidirect.gov.uk/articles/careers-health-and-social-care-introduction
- Royal College of Nursing *RCN Careers Resources*: www.rcn.org.uk/professional-development/your-career

*Table 1.2: Nursing and midwifery job titles*

| Area | Example job titles |
| --- | --- |
| Clinical | *Nursing:*<br>Staff nurse, sister/charge nurse (CN), deputy sister/CN, registered staff nurse, team leader, clinical lead, lead practitioner, clinical pathway/discharge coordinator, senior nurse, clinical services manager, matron, nurse consultant, non-medical prescriber, head of care, head of care and quality, clinical governance practitioner<br><br>*Midwifery:*<br>Registered midwife, integrated midwife, lead midwife, caseload midwife, labour ward coordinator, labour ward lead manager, delivery suite coordinator, community midwife, head of midwifery, associate director of nursing and midwifery, director of midwifery |
| Education | Practice development nurse/midwife, clinical nurse/midwifery educator, clinical educator, education lead, nurse/midwife educator, lead in clinical education, practice nurse/midwifery educator, education facilitator, lecturer practitioner, education practitioner |

*Table 1.2: (continued)*

| Area | Example job titles |
|---|---|
| Specialist | Specialist practitioner, specialist nurse/midwife, specialist nurse/midwifery practitioner, advanced nurse/midwifery practitioner, senior advanced nurse/midwifery practitioner, screening coordinator, professional midwifery/nursing advocate |
| Research | Research nurse/midwife, research practitioner, specialist research nurse/midwife, clinical researcher, senior research nurse/midwife, research lead, research fellow, research delivery coordinator, clinical studies nurse/midwife, clinical trials nurse/midwife, lead research investigating nurse/midwife |

## ☰ KEY TIPS

- Do not choose or discount a role or career pathway until you have a full understanding of what it actually involves.
- Decide whether a role or career pathway suits your skill set and personal needs by accessing accurate information and career advice.

### 1.2.6 Strategies to help you choose the right role and career pathway

#### Gain insights from staff working in the role/field

- Talk to staff working in the role/field that you wish to pursue. Talk to several staff to gain a realistic overview and identify advantages and disadvantages from their perspective, to establish whether the role will meet your expectations.
- Establish what qualifications are required for a post/career pathway by speaking to nurses already established in the area, e.g. a 'nurse prescribing' module for a specialist nurse role.

#### Review online/local resources

- Review national and local online career resources and websites (see links just above *Table 1.2*).
- Watch online videos from specialist areas by staff, patient groups and charities.
- Check out the global and national picture in relation to a setting or role, by thinking about questions such as:
  - What national, government and professional changes are being planned?
  - Is a service about to amalgamate with another?

- – Are beds, wards or services to close in the future?
- – Is a specialist service going to be reconfigured?
- Healthcare services are continually changing and future plans may suit you, or lead you to reconsider your options.
- Read about future plans on employer/Trust websites, local newspapers and newsletters, e.g. regarding whether services are expanding or relocating.

## Arrange informal visits

- Arrange informal visits in a variety of areas to observe staff with patients; get a feel for differences between roles/areas and decide whether one suits your needs.
- Informal visits consist of a meeting and walk around an area/ community setting that is led by a senior nurse or practice educator, to discuss what an area will offer you.
- Be wary of applying for any job if they will not allow you to have an informal visit.
- During visits make sure that you talk to current staff and new starters about the support offered *(talk to several people as you may pick the one person who is happy/not happy)*.
- Contact the manager/educator by email/telephone to secure an appropriate time for your visit *(senior staff need to prioritise their services and you may not receive a response straight away)*.
- During informal visits ask yourself key questions, such as:
  - – Can I work with the staff/patients in the area?
  - – Is the type of work suited to my skills set?
  - – Do I prefer medical/surgical, acute/long-term, community- or hospital-based care?
  - – Does the setting offer me enough flexibility on the rota for my hobby once a week?
  - – Are they offering me a good orientation, continued support and development?
  - – What are the prospects for future career development and senior posts?
  - – Were staff positive about the support they received?

## Attend recruitment events/careers fairs

- Attend open days and recruitment events/careers fairs, as employers will present what they can offer you, a potential applicant.

- Recruitment events are especially helpful to staff who are unsure about what they want to pursue. They are a great way to compare and contrast areas and roles, if you are still unsure.

## Observe or shadow staff at work

- Observing and shadowing a staff member is the best way to gain insights into the day-to-day reality of what a role actually entails, which may help you choose an appropriate career pathway. You may not realise, for example, that a particular advanced specialist nurse spends a large amount of time advising staff on the telephone during their working week.
- Use observational visits as opportunities to network and demonstrate your interest in the area. You may be offered additional time in the field, e.g. attending patient education groups.
- When applying for jobs it is good to state that you gained an interest through shadowing, as it demonstrates enthusiasm and motivation.
- Information gained during shadowing will help you answer questions in future interviews if you are asked about what you know about a role/field (see *Step 5*).

## Review support offered

- Identify areas that have dedicated educators and/or a structured plan of support that will be helpful to your development.
- Establish a global picture of opportunities for support and career development across the service through discussion with experienced staff:
  - Do they have practice educators, practice development nurses/ midwives or clinical educators who support new starters?
  - What structured support is in place and how will it be delivered?
- Do not dismiss an area that does not have an educator role, as they may have excellent team leaders or managers to support you. Smaller teams may not have the finances or need the role.
- Be wary of applying to any area if the senior nurse cannot answer how they are going to support and develop you.
- Ask the senior nurse or clinical educator to email you their programmes of support if they do not have hard copies to show you on a visit. This will be helpful if you want to compare offers across a number of potential posts from different areas.

## Try roles out through rotations

- If you have had a narrow range of student placements, or are uncertain about where to specialise or develop your career, it may be helpful to structure a post as a rotation.
- Usually rotations are set up between two or three areas, and you spend 6–9 months in each area. More health service employers are offering bespoke rotations on request, e.g. two areas over 2 years.
- A rotation does not suit all nurses, as they can feel unsettled moving between areas. Others find rotations invaluable to help them decide which career pathway would be best for them.

## Make the most of progress reviews and appraisals

- Discuss which career pathway is best suited to your skill set during progression review meetings, which will inform your future development plans.
- Ask your line manager to support your career progression and offer learning and development advice.
- Arrange an annual appraisal to discuss your current role and set objectives, individualised development plans and SMART goals (see further guidance in *Step 2, Section 2.4*).

## Identify the academic level and experience required to progress

- Review local job descriptions and personal specifications to establish the 'essential' and 'desirable' experience, skills and qualifications required for the role you desire.
- Can you meet the requirements of the role or do you want to work towards them later? For example, studying for a master's, whilst working full time, may not be feasible currently.
- Establish which areas are most likely to offer you funding for an essential course, as a university module will cost you hundreds of pounds if you decide to self-fund.
- Align your future practice and development towards achieving the required qualification, experience and clinical skills (see *Table 1.4*). If another setting offers you more chance of courses or relevant experience in your chosen area, then consider a move.

**Identify someone to give you constructive, sound and positive career advice**

- Identify an appropriate person in your setting to give you career advice to aid your progression. This may be your preceptor, line manager, an educator or clinical supervisor.
- Listen to feedback from your manager/preceptor, as you may not yet have the required skills to progress. If you do not agree with the advice you are offered, or are unsure, do not hesitate to ask an independent senior nurse or educator what they think too.

# 1.3 THE DIFFERENCES BETWEEN BANDS AND ROLES

Due to the diverse nature of nursing and midwifery today, and the lack of standardisation of roles across the UK, you may become confused by the different job titles. Most nursing roles relate to one of four key areas, as follows:
- Clinical
- Specialist
- Research
- Education.

Examples of nursing and midwifery roles are presented under each of the four areas in *Table 1.2*. Roles may cross over areas or have a mixture of responsibilities, e.g. a lecturer practitioner role split as 50% education and 50% clinical or an advanced nurse practitioner's role split as 40% research and 60% advanced practice. What encompasses 'clinical' in a role may range from hands-on patient care delivering fundamental care needs, to managing a large number of clinical staff with minimal direct patient care.

## 1.3.1 Differences between nursing bands 2–4

It is essential that team members understand the differences between banding, qualifications and the competence levels of other members of their team when delegating care. Firstly, it is important to have an overview of band 2 to 4 nursing and midwifery roles utilised within your local setting, to plan the progression of junior staff you are responsible for.

Checking the generic job descriptions of band 2s to 4s when you first start in an area is helpful to give you a general insight into the differences between bands. Typical generic differences in roles and responsibilities between bands 2 to 4 are presented in *Table 1.3*; however, roles may vary depending on your employer.

*Table 1.3: Differences between bands 2 to 4*

| Nursing band | Key responsibilities |
|---|---|
| Band 2 | • Nursing assistants, carers or support workers are responsible for supporting the RN to deliver routine care to patients, such as:<br>  – contributing to the provision of a welcoming environment for staff, patients and their families<br>  – answering the telephone politely and sensitively, and informing the supervising RN/RM promptly<br>  – recording clinical information in patient records, e.g. fluid balance and nutritional charts<br>  – maintaining a safe and efficient working environment, especially with regard to infection control<br>  – undertaking delegated tasks, when trained and declared competent, and being aware of the responsibilities and limitations of their band 2 *(defined in local job descriptions)*<br>  – maintaining good communication and working relationships with staff, patients, relatives and visitors<br>• The role of a maternity support worker (MSW) (in addition to the above) is to assist midwives in caring for women and their babies throughout the vital stages of pregnancy, childbirth and the first few days of birth *(defined in local job descriptions)* |
| Band 3 | *Nursing:*<br>• There are currently local differences between the roles of band 3 nurses in the UK, and no standard registration of the role<br>• Band 3s usually undertake advanced skills through additional training, e.g. level 3 National Vocational Qualification (NVQ) or a national Care Certificate *(the latter consists of 15 standards of learning outcomes and competencies expected of a nursing assistant)*<br>• A band 3 actively contributes to care planning by liaising with the RN; however, they are always under the direct leadership of an RN. They may take on additional roles, according to signed competencies and relevant training, e.g. supporting junior new starters and doing observations<br><br>*Midwifery:*<br>• The Royal College of Midwives (RCM, 2016b) clearly lists tasks that can be carried out by a MSW in the document *The Roles and Responsibilities of MSWs*<br>• On completion of competencies and training, MSWs may assist midwives with venepuncture, cannulation, blood glucose, observations and support breast feeding<br>• MSWs may undertake advanced skills and additional level 2 and 3 NVQ health and social care training |
| Band 4 | *Nursing:*<br>• Band 4 nurses may be called assistant practitioners or nursing associates<br>• Assistant practitioners work alongside band 2/3 nurses and RNs to deliver fundamental aspects of care, defined by employers<br>• Assistant practitioners are unable to deliver areas of care within the remit of an associate nurse or RN, such as administering medications<br>• Band 4 nursing associates have a higher level of knowledge and skill to band 2/3 and band 4 assistant practitioners<br>• Nursing associates work both independently and with the multidisciplinary team (MDT), to deliver care that is always under the direct leadership of an RN |

*Table 1.3: (continued)*

| Nursing band | Key responsibilities |
|---|---|
| | • Nursing associates can deliver some elements of clinical work that have previously been within the remit of RNs, such as:<br>  – performing patient assessments from admission to discharge and writing patient care plans<br>  – recording and interpreting observations and escalating concerns<br>  – assessing and monitoring patients' skin integrity and reporting/documenting changes<br>  – recognising changes in a patient's condition and reporting to a registered nurse/medic<br>  – performing, understanding and reporting patient risk assessments<br>  – actively participating in handover to ensure continuity of care<br>  – using equipment and medical devices (following appropriate training)<br>  – demonstrating understanding of informed consent, mental capacity act and deprivation of liberty during care<br>  – engaging in reflective practice<br>• Nursing associates complete a level 5 health and social care (H&SC) foundation degree, which enables them to administer medications when signed off as competent *(this currently does not include intravenous (IV) medications)*<br>• The nursing associate 2-year level 5 H&SC foundation degree adheres to new NMC (2018) *Standards of Proficiency for Nursing Associates*. In July 2018, the Nursing and Midwifery Council (NMC) became the legal regulator for nursing associates, who will be placed on a nursing associate register<br>• There are no plans to regulate nursing associates in Scotland, Wales or Northern Ireland<br><br>*Midwifery:*<br>• The RCM (2016a) does not currently support a band 4 midwifery associate role for MSWs, although there are band 4 assistant midwifery practitioner jobs advertised by some employers *(check local band 4 job descriptions for responsibilities)*<br>• There are plans underway for a more clearly demarcated set of national developmental competencies to progress MSWs within the parameters of band 2 to 4 |

## 1.3.2 Differences between nursing bands 5 to 9

Whatever your chosen field, you will work within a team of RNs/RMs who will range in banding from band 5 upwards. All band 5 RNs/RMs must have completed a level 6 nursing or midwifery degree, in comparison to the level 5 foundation degree requirement of a band 4.

Specific job descriptions and person specifications will give you information about registered roles in your area. Typical generic differences in roles and responsibilities between bands 5 to 9 are shown below (adapted from Forde-Johnston, 2018).

## Band 5

- Delivering high quality patient care adhering to national and local, legal and professional requirements
- Delivering care for a named group of patients, babies, mothers or parents
- Responsible for own caseload under indirect supervision of senior nurse/midwife
- Professionally accountable for assessing, planning, implementing and evaluating patient care, using patient care plans and the Nursing Process
- Supervising and teaching students, unregistered nurses/midwives and nursing associates/assistant practitioners
- Collaboratively working with an MDT to facilitate effective care
- Utilising evidence-based practice
- Promoting patient wellbeing through education and health promotion
- Providing family-centred care and support for relatives/carers/parents.

## Band 6

- Responsible for delivering patient-focused care (as Band 5), whilst also influencing the delivery of care by others in their team, e.g. supporting a team of colleagues
- Responsible for supporting the senior nurse/midwife to assist with managing, developing and leading the service (may deputise for senior nurse/midwife)
- Acting as a professional role model
- Contributing to the provision and maintenance of high standards in the clinical setting
- Using initiative to organise and prioritise workloads of others, e.g. shift coordinator or monitoring standards
- Responsible for inducting/supporting/developing a group of staff.

## Band 7

- Responsible for delivering high standards of patient care across their service (as above)
- Providing clinical leadership and management of a nursing/midwifery ward team/service
- Effectively supporting Band 8
- Responsible for the day-to-day management of a ward/service and providing effective management of resources
- Budget holding for staff and services

- Responsible for maintaining compliance with national and local, professional and legal standards and targets
- Ensuring adherence to local and national policies and guidelines.

## Band 8

- Strategically plans clinical services
- Responsible for day-to-day organisation and delivery in clinical departments/settings to meet local and national targets
- Supporting initiatives within the service whilst providing clear direction for staff
- Responsible for deployment, motivation, development and performance of all clinical staff across their services
- Ensuring the achievement of CQC standards.

(Nurse consultants and educational leads at band 8 will have similar responsibilities linked to educational or patient care pathway targets.)

## Band 9

- Directing services and managing and leading all bands (8 and below) within their service.
- Reporting to the managing director to develop and implement changes within a strategic framework
- Ensuring financial targets are achieved across all services
- Responsible for developing the strategic vision and transformation plans in the local healthcare system
- Ensuring operational and clinical services are delivered and quality is assured
- Responsible for ensuring safe and effective patient-centred care is delivered
- Providing detailed analysis of the sustainability of future services
- Promoting innovations that can enhance the service.

### *1.3.3 Align your career to relevant skills and qualifications*

Having a clear understanding of a job description, which includes essential or desirable personal specifications, will help you decide whether a role or career pathway suits your development plans. You can then align your experience and transferable skills to what an employer and interviewer will be looking for. You cannot expect to meet the criteria for shortlisting, or demonstrate insight into a role at interview, without fully understanding what you are applying for.

The earlier you start to align professional and academic requirements with a career pathway, the more chance you have of successfully achieving your aspirations. Obviously, not everyone has ambitions to rise up the career ladder, and you may have no desire to move from your band 5 RN/RM role following registration. This decision should be respected, as band 5s are essential to the delivery of patient services. However, all staff are still required to keep their clinical skills up to date through post-registration courses and study days applicable to their role.

Example career pathways from band 5 to 9 for four key areas: clinical, education, advanced practice and research, are presented in *Tables 1.4–1.7*. Each career pathway aligns banding to example professional development and academic courses. Always check local job descriptions when applying for posts or deciding which career pathway is suitable. Employers will establish 'desirable' and 'essential' professional and academic requirements for individual jobs. The academic courses listed in *Table 1.4* are ideal, and some employers will not request this academic level prior to shortlisting for interviews and/or may allocate different banding to different job titles.

*Table 1.4: Example clinical post career pathways aligned to professional development and education*

| CLINICAL POST | | |
|---|---|---|
| **Nursing band and posts** | **Professional development** | **Academic course** |
| Band 5: staff nurse, registered nurse or registered midwife | • NMC registered<br>• Interest shown in specialist area | • BSc nursing or midwifery degree |
| Band 6: senior staff nurse/midwife, deputy sister/CN | • NMC registered<br>• Experienced 1–2 years in specialist area<br>• Supervising and assessing in practice<br>• Active interest demonstrated in area, e.g. 'link role' or assisted band 7s<br>• Completed service project in the area | • BSc nursing or midwifery degree<br>• Post-qualification certificate in specialist area, e.g. oncology, or teaching and assessing<br>• Postgraduate diploma in management/leadership/public health/finance |
| Band 7: nursing or midwifery sister/CN | • NMC registered<br>• Experienced 2–3 years in specialist area<br>• Previously worked as band 6<br>• Supervising and assessing in practice<br>• Leadership or project management experience<br>• Experience managing teams/others | • BSc nursing or midwifery degree<br>• Postgraduate certificate in specialist area or management/leadership<br>• Postgraduate diploma<br>• Master's relating to healthcare, leadership, management, public health or finance |

*Table 1.4: (continued)*

| CLINICAL POST | | |
|---|---|---|
| **Nursing band and posts** | **Professional development** | **Academic course** |
| Band 8/9: matron/ divisional nurse or midwife | • NMC registered<br>• Experienced 3–5 years in healthcare (not necessarily the specialist area)<br>• Supervising and assessing in practice to meet service targets/improve performance<br>• Experience as a band 7 delivering and leading nursing or midwifery teams<br>• Demonstrates leadership, management or project management experience<br>• Experience of financial management or writing business plans | • BSc nursing or midwifery degree<br>• Postgraduate diploma in leadership, finance or project management<br>• Master's relating to advanced nursing or midwifery practice, healthcare, leadership, management, public health or finance |

*Table 1.5: Example educational post career pathways aligned to professional development and education*

| EDUCATIONAL POST | | |
|---|---|---|
| **Nursing band and post** | **Professional development** | **Academic course** |
| Band 5: staff nurse, registered nurse or registered midwife | • NMC registered<br>• Interest shown in education | • BSc nursing or midwifery degree |
| Band 6: practice development nurse/midwife, clinical nurse/ midwifery educator, clinical educator | • NMC registered<br>• Experienced 1–2 years in healthcare<br>• Supervising and assessing in practice<br>• Active interest demonstrated in education e.g. 'educator link role', delivered teaching or written educational documents, such as competencies | • BSc nursing or midwifery degree<br>• Post-qualification certificate in education<br>• Postgraduate certificate in education |
| Band 7: practice development education lead, corporate educator, education facilitator | • NMC registered<br>• Experienced 2–3 years in healthcare<br>• Previously worked in a band 6 education role (an education role may link to transferable skills, e.g. a team leader may demonstrate teaching within a team)<br>• Supervising and assessing in practice<br>• Leadership or project management experience<br>• Experience managing others | • BSc nursing or midwifery degree<br>• Postgraduate certificate in education<br>• Postgraduate diploma, ideally master's relating to healthcare, leadership, education or management |

**Table 1.5:** *(continued)*

| EDUCATIONAL POST | | |
|---|---|---|
| **Nursing band and post** | **Professional development** | **Academic course** |
| Band 8/9: corporate/ Trust divisional education lead/lecturer practitioner | • NMC registered<br>• Experienced 3–5 years in healthcare field<br>• Supervising and assessing in practice to meet service targets/improve standards<br>• Experience planning and delivering educational programmes<br>• Leadership, management or project management experience<br>• Experience managing teams<br>• Experience of financial management and writing business plans | • Health-related (Hons) degree (could be nurse, midwife or other allied health professional (AHP))<br>• Corporate/Trust divisional education lead should have master's relating to healthcare leadership, education or management<br>• Lecturer practitioner should have master's in education, advanced practice or healthcare; usually working towards, or completed, a doctorate/PhD |

**Table 1.6:** *Example advanced practice career pathways aligned to professional development and education*

| SPECIALIST/ADVANCED NURSING PRACTICE POST | | |
|---|---|---|
| **Nursing band and post** | **Professional development** | **Academic course** |
| Band 5: staff nurse, registered nurse or registered midwife | • NMC registered<br>• Interest shown in specialist area | • BSc nursing or midwifery degree |
| Band 6: trainee specialist nurse, clinical governance nurse or midwife (without MSc) | • NMC registered<br>• Experienced 1 year in specialist field<br>• Supervising and assessing in practice<br>• Active interest demonstrated in specialist area e.g. 'link role' in the area or related service improvement/ research project | • BSc nursing or midwifery degree<br>• Post-qualification certificate in specialist area<br>• Accredited nurse prescribing qualification or course<br>• Postgraduate diploma in advanced nursing practice or autonomous healthcare practice |
| Band 7: advanced nurse or midwifery practitioner; clinical nurse/ midwifery specialist; clinical governance lead | • NMC registered<br>• Experienced 2–3 years in specialist field<br>• Previously worked in a band 6 role<br>• Supervising and assessing in practice<br>• Leadership or project management experience<br>• Experience managing others | • BSc nursing or midwifery degree<br>• Post-qualification certificate in specialist area<br>• Accredited nurse prescribing qualification or course<br>• Postgraduate diploma<br>• Master's in autonomous healthcare practice or advanced nursing practice |

*Table 1.6: (continued)*

| SPECIALIST/ADVANCED NURSING PRACTICE POST | | |
|---|---|---|
| **Nursing band and post** | **Professional development** | **Academic course** |
| Band 8/9: service manager to senior advanced nurse or midwifery practitioner/ nurse or midwifery consultant | • NMC registered<br>• Experienced 3–5 years in healthcare field<br>• Preferable to have experience in specialist area (not always essential if transferable skills can be shown)<br>• Supervising and assessing to meet specialist service standards/improve specialist services<br>• Project management experience<br>• Leadership and managerial experience<br>• Experience managing teams<br>• Experience of financial management | • BSc nursing or midwifery degree<br>• Accredited qualification in management, leadership or project management<br>• Masters in autonomous healthcare practice or advanced nursing or midwifery practice<br>• Nurse consultant should have master's and doctorate/PhD (or working towards doctorate) |

*Table 1.7: Example research post career pathways aligned to professional development and education*

| RESEARCH POST | | |
|---|---|---|
| **Nursing band and post** | **Professional development** | **Academic course** |
| Band 5: research nurse/ midwife | • NMC registered<br>• Interest shown in research or specialist area | • BSc (Hons) nursing or midwifery degree |
| Band 6: clinical research nurse/ midwife, clinical trials nurse/ midwife or senior/deputy researcher | • NMC registered<br>• Experienced 1 year in healthcare field<br>• Supervising and assessing in practice<br>• Experience in specialist area, e.g. endocrinology if diabetes research post<br>• Active interest demonstrated in research area, e.g. link role or research project | • BSc (Hons) nursing or midwifery degree<br>• Research course/qualification<br>• Post-qualification certificate or diploma in specialist area |
| Band 7: clinical research practitioner, research project manager, trials project manager | • NMC/AHP registered qualification<br>• Experienced 2–3 years in healthcare field<br>• Supervising and assessing in practice<br>• Previously worked in a band 6 role<br>• Research and project management experience<br>• Leadership experience<br>• Experience managing others | • Health-related (Hons) degree (could be nurse, midwife or other AHP)<br>• Research module/course<br>• Post-qualification certificate or diploma in specialist area<br>• Project management or leadership qualification<br>• Postgraduate diploma<br>• Health-related master's |

*Table 1.7: (continued)*

| RESEARCH POST | | |
|---|---|---|
| **Nursing band and post** | **Professional development** | **Academic course** |
| Band 8: clinical research operational manager/ research team service manager | • NMC/AHP registered qualification<br>• Experienced 3–5 years in healthcare field<br>• Supervising and assessing to meet research service standards/outcomes<br>• Previously worked in a band 7 role<br>• Preferable to have experience in specialist area but not always essential<br>• Project management experience<br>• Leadership and managerial experience<br>• Experience managing teams and finances | • Health-related (Hons) degree (could be nurse or other AHP)<br>• Research qualification<br>• Project management qualification<br>• Master's in leadership, management or finance<br>• Working towards doctorate/PhD |

## WHAT TO DO NEXT

1. Establish what roles, specialist fields and career pathways are available to you locally/nationally with your current qualifications and level of professional experience. You may not take the career route you originally planned, and it is important to review what is out there in case you choose to change direction later.
2. Reflect on your career journey so far and think about which roles/courses/career pathways suit your interests, skills and strengths. Discuss your professional and academic development with an experienced member of staff and educator, as part of a professional development review (PDR).
3. Establish what jobs, courses or career pathways actually entail, before deciding on which path to take. You may do this through attending informal visits, undertaking a rotation post, talking to staff in the roles you aspire to, and reviewing documentation relating to a specific role/course/career pathway.

## REFERENCES AND FURTHER READING

Forde-Johnston, C. (2018) *How to Thrive as a Newly Qualified Nurse.* Lantern Publishing.

Health and Social Care Information Centre (2018) *NHS Vacancy Statistics England: February 2015–March 2018, Provisional Experimental Statistics.* HSCIC.

House of Commons Health Committee (2018) *The Nursing Workforce: second report of session 2017–2019.* Available at: https://publications. parliament.uk/pa/cm201719/cmselect/cmhealth/353/353.pdf [accessed 4 December 2019]

King's Fund (2017) *Why we shouldn't panic about nursing students... yet* Available at: www.kingsfund.org.uk/blog/2017/07/why-we-shouldnt-panic-about-nursing-students-yet [accessed 4 December 2019]

NHS Improvement (2018) *Performance of the NHS provider sector for the quarter ended 30 June 2018.* Available at: https://improvement.nhs.uk/ documents/3209/Performance_of_the_NHS_provider_sector_for_the_ month_ended_30_June_18_FINAL.pdf [accessed 4 December 2019]

Nursing and Midwifery Council (2018) *Standards of Proficiency for Nursing Associates.* Available at: www.nmc.org.uk/globalassets/ sitedocuments/education-standards/nursing-associates-proficiency-standards.pdf [accessed 4 December 2019]

Royal College of Midwives (2016a) *Getting the Midwifery Workforce Right.* Available at: www.rcm.org.uk/media/2368/getting-the-midwifery-workforce-right.pdf [accessed 4 December 2019]

Royal College of Midwives (2016b) *The Roles and Responsibilities of Maternity Support Workers.* Available at: www.rcm.org.uk/ media/2338/role-responsibilities-maternity-support-workers.pdf [accessed 4 December 2019]

Royal College of Nursing (2017) *The UK Nursing Labour Market Review 2017.* Available at: www.rcn.org.uk/-/media/royal-college-of-nursing/documents/publications/2017/december/pdf-006625.pdf [accessed 4 December 2019]

UCAS (2018) *2019 Cycle Applicant Figures – June Deadline.* Available at: www.ucas.com/corporate/data-and-analysis/ucas-undergraduate-releases/2018-cycle-applicant-figures-june-deadline [accessed 4 December 2019]

Willis, P. (2012) *Raising the Bar: shape of caring – a review of the future education and training of registered nurses and care assistants.* Health Education England. Available at: www.hee.nhs.uk/sites/default/ files/documents/2348-Shape-of-caring-review-FINAL.pdf [accessed 4 December 2019]

# DRIVE YOUR OWN DEVELOPMENT

*"Our ambition should be to rule ourselves, the true kingdom
for each one of us; and true progress is to know more,
and be more, and to do more."*
Oscar Wilde (1854–1900), Irish poet/playwright

## 2.1 THE IMPORTANCE OF LIFELONG LEARNING TO YOUR CAREER DEVELOPMENT

Oscar Wilde's quote highlights the need to direct our career *'to rule ourselves'* and pursue our chosen career *'ambition'*. Lifelong learning requires healthcare practitioners to develop over time, *'to know more'*, and practically apply theory to *'do more'*. A lifelong commitment to improving your knowledge, skills and competence will inform your career aspirations and professional practice. This includes reflecting on clinical experiences with others, and aligning professional development and academic study to a career pathway.

When planning your future goals, you should aim to complete qualifications and work-based projects in your current role that align to your future career aspirations. A newly qualified RN/RM, for example, usually requires a minimum of 6 months to 1 year post-registration experience, evidence of being a 'link nurse' and/or the completion of a local project, before applying for a post-registration specialist course. Nowadays, many band 7 to 8 roles require master's level academic study, which will be detailed in the job description. To avoid future disappointment, it is important that you seek accurate advice to plan your future professional and academic development.

- When planning your future goals, find out in advance what is required to progress, in order to prevent disappointment. Avoid the frustration of finding out you do not meet the criteria to be shortlisted when you download an application for your ideal role or course.

### 2.1.1 Plan your development a year in advance

There will be times during your career when you require immediate training and direction from others, such as when you are new to a role or need to learn a new skill. At other times, you need to plan your long-term development for a current role or future position. 'Essential' training and education courses are usually fully funded by employers, whilst those that are 'desirable' may be funded or may have to be self-funded. At whatever stage of your career, you are accountable for directing your own learning that needs to be planned a year in advance to secure course places, course funding or paid study leave.

Although *Step 2* states '*drive your own development*', this does not mean that you should plan your learning and development in isolation. It is essential that you collaborate with others, engage with local and national educational structures, and call on the advice of experienced role models. Utilising available support will enable you to establish:

- what you need to know in your current role
- what professional/academic courses are essential or desirable
- how to access course places, course funding and study leave
- which role/career pathway is the best choice for you
- how to progress in the future
- who can support your career
- what additional resources will support your goals.

Although employers should support your current essential training and development needs, they are not obliged to support additional 'non-essential' or desirable courses or study days. As with all health service budgets, there are annual limits to education funding and study leave, which means access to course places is often competitive. You should always register your professional development plans in an appraisal and professional development review (PDR), and plan course funding applications a year in advance.

---

📋 **KEY TIPS**

- Plan your learning and development proactively a year in advance through appraisals and PDRs.
- Find out how to navigate local communication systems to book meetings with relevant staff who can support your progression.

This chapter provides simple pointers to help you navigate complex educational and professional structures more easily, to give you the best chance of reaching your goals in the future!

## 2.2 UNDERSTAND HOW TO NAVIGATE EDUCATIONAL STRUCTURES

### 2.2.1 *Immediate versus long-term training and development*

Prior to accessing local learning and development advice, you should be aware that information will relate either to your immediate learning and development, or long-term continuing development. Simple questions are provided below that can be used as a basis for discussion with educators and managers:

1. Your immediate learning, development and training needs:
   - What knowledge/skills do I need in my role now and in the near future?
   - Is my statutory/mandatory training up to date? Where do I find this information?
   - Is my NMC registration and revalidation up to date? Where do I find this information?
   - Do I have an induction checklist, or in-house specialist training to complete in my new role?
   - Do I have role-specific competencies, vocational standards or key performance indicators (KPIs) to achieve? If so, who will assess me and sign them off?
   - Does my role require specialist training? If yes, how do I book training?
   - Who will support my immediate professional development and offer feedback on my current performance? How is this feedback given and how often?
   - If I feel overwhelmed in my role who do I go to? What additional support will my employer offer me?

2.  Your continuing professional development and long-term career planning:
    -   Who is my line manager and who completes my annual appraisal?
    -   Where do I see myself in the future and which career pathway do I plan to work towards? (see *Step 1, Tables 1.4–1.7* for career pathways).
    -   Who will guide my continuing education, development and career plans?
    -   What study days, short professional courses and university accredited courses will support my development plans?
    -   What is the process for obtaining financial support and paid study time on continuing courses?
    -   Are there opportunities for access to a career coach, clinical supervision or other support group within my local area?

### 2.2.2 Check what is available to support your career goals

Your learning and development will stall without regular structured support, at whatever band you are. Reputable healthcare employers nurture and develop their staff in order to retain employees and assure a highly skilled and effectively functioning workforce. Under the seven pillars of clinical governance *'education and training'* and *'staffing and staff management'* are highlighted (Nicholls *et al.*, 2000), to ensure that individual staff members are skilled, self-efficient, responsible and accountable. NHS systems and frameworks that aim to maintain standards and improve care quality are further detailed in *Table 3.4*. An overview of key terms and related references is presented, including: quality improvement, clinical governance, clinical audit, quality standards, risk management and change management models.

It still surprises me how some individuals are oblivious to the support and development opportunities being offered by local employers and national professional bodies. They are upset when someone less experienced is offered a sought-after secondment or course fees. However, they have not been regularly checking their work emails or reading posters advertising local opportunities.

Many employers communicate opportunities to staff electronically through email or intranet sites, or via posters in handover rooms. Some employers offer open lunchtime forums or evening events publicising new career opportunities, which are advertised in local papers. To increase your chances of applying for fully funded post-registration master's modules, leadership/research secondments or specialist training courses, you must engage with the communication systems being used to disseminate learning and development opportunities.

 **KEY TIP**

- Make an effort to keep up to date with what is going on locally and nationally to utilise opportunities on offer. If you do not regularly engage with employer and management communication systems, you risk missing out on future opportunities.

### 2.2.3  Go support and inspire others!

I regularly meet junior staff who express a wish to develop their career, but who were not encouraged by colleagues or given the correct information. This may be due to staff being too busy at the time or not knowing what is available to advise them. I offer regular career advisory sessions to staff within a hospital Trust and start with four simple tips to help them access support (see below). These tips are relevant whatever band you are and can be shared with colleagues. Sometimes, it just takes one positive conversation in a coffee room or one flyer on a communication board/email attachment to inspire someone to pursue their goals.

 **KEY TIP**

- Every staff member has a responsibility to support their colleagues to enable them to develop and thrive in their role. Whatever level/band you are, go and find out about available career pathways/courses and inspire others to pursue their career ambitions!

### 2.2.4  Four tips to access support

#### Find out who is responsible for guiding learning and development

- The Care Quality Commission (CQC) requires that all healthcare employers offer adequate training and development to ensure staff are safe and competent.
- Whatever your role/banding, you should be allocated a minimum of one named person, to support your PDRs.

- Find out who is responsible for the following:
  - your annual appraisal
  - guiding induction, orientation and statutory/mandatory training
  - assessing and feeding back on your performance, e.g. signing off role-specific competencies, Flying Start NHS portfolio evidence, PDRs, performance improvement plans (PIPs), NMC revalidation
  - organising in-house skills training
  - offering clinical training if you require extra practice support
  - organising in-house coaching, mentoring, clinical supervision or staff support groups
  - disseminating information about future learning and development opportunities
  - authorising attendance on study days/courses and funding external courses
  - organising practice supervision of others.
- It is acceptable to have a variety of staff for support, as long as roles are clearly defined.
- If staff guiding your development do not communicate with each other, e.g. one person states you are doing well while another says you are not competent, you have every right to request a more cohesive approach.

## Establish how educational team structures work

- There should be a visual representation of educational hierarchy on employer intranet sites. It is helpful to understand global structures in case you want a second opinion or educators are off sick in your area.
- Employers have corporate education teams for key areas, such as: preceptorship, clinical skills training, international nurse assessments, clinical supervision, coaching, eLearning, student placement facilitators and leadership development.
- Some private healthcare companies do not provide in-house education and expect individuals to self-fund essential training.
- Employer education leads are responsible for the management of education budgets and structuring of education.
- Education and management leads in each institution/community setting will decide how education budgets are allocated and which external courses are funded following local training needs analysis (TNA).
- If you wish to apply for course funding or approved study time you will need to know the following:
  - Do I need to have the course/study days requested and documented on my appraisal or PDR?

- – What is the process for requesting course funding or study leave?
- – What are the deadlines for applications and is there an application form that needs to be signed by my line manager?
- – Is there a restriction on places and what are the criteria for applying?
- Will I need to go through an in-house or university interview?

## Use local and national communication systems

- Establish how local/national communications systems work regarding education and training and learn how to use systems competently, e.g. Flying Start NHS for newly qualified nurses, midwives and allied health professionals in Scotland.
- Employers use online eLearning resources and electronic learning management systems (eLMS) within local intranet sites to disseminate information under key headings such as: 'staff education', 'training' and/or 'professional development'. Find out how to browse information and manage your user account fully.
- Employers use 'document stores' and hold details on intranet sites such as: study days/courses, application/booking procedures, support structures/groups and learning resources/training packages.
- Statutory/mandatory training is essential and you are responsible for keeping 'in date'. Most employers use an eLearning red/amber/green warning system informing you that essential training will be out of date in the next month/week/day. You can be performance managed if essential training consistently remains out of date. Check your emails and never ignore 'out of date' warnings.
- RNs/RMs must ensure their NMC registration is in date, including revalidation every 3 years (see *Section 2.6*).
- You are responsible for booking non-essential professional development courses. You will require line manager approval if you need study time away from your clinical service, e.g. a signed application request form.
- Some managers manually book you onto in-house courses or offer places to a set number of staff, to ensure services are covered. Find out what system is used and who is responsible for authorising course bookings.
- Find out what processes are used to complete PDRs and appraisals; many employers use online systems.
- When applying for course funding, adhere to deadlines which are highlighted on emails/local intranet sites.
- Ensure work email passwords are up to date, in order to access information and marketing material.

- Line managers require advance notice to complete an appraisal, course reference or sign a funding application. Some managers stipulate that funding will only be offered if a discussion has taken place within an appraisal/PDR.
- Book a slot with relevant staff in advance and check when managers have annual leave booked or who is deputising in their absence, to avoid missing deadlines.

## Access advice and support from others throughout your career

- Throughout your career it is important that you access advice/support from others to:
  - confidentially share your concerns, to prevent stress/burnout (see *Section 6.2.4*)
  - gain constructive feedback on your performance to develop your competence and skills
  - obtain career advice to aid your future progression.
- You may require different support as you progress through your career, from different people, according to their skills set and knowledge base, e.g. a lead educator may advise on a course deadline, as opposed to your line manager.
- Network and identify local/national colleagues to offer sound and professional advice. A good role model will acknowledge your concerns, whilst constructively suggesting strategies to inform your future learning.
- Network with past lecturers, corporate leads or experienced nurses from other areas, to receive an alternative perspective.
- Use established structures for practice support in your local area, such as:
  - clinical supervision – a safe and confidential environment for you to reflect on practice and discuss issues from work. All RNs/RMs should have access to clinical supervision for the duration of their career to enable them to develop their knowledge, skills and competence in practice. A clinical supervisor may be allocated to supervise you individually or within a clinical supervision group. Some employers will allocate you a clinical supervisor, whereas others will wait for you to request one (see further detail relating to clinical supervision in *Table 3.2*).
  - Coaching – a more short-term approach where a trained coach helps you to understand a situation more clearly, to develop new

ideas and to take future action. The main aim of coaching is to improve your performance at work. Coaching usually lasts for a short period (3–8 sessions) and focuses on specific skills and goals. Employers are not obliged to offer individual coaching and there are private coaching companies available.

- Group forums – an opportunity to meet peers in a group that targets a certain band, role or profession. Group forums promote reassurance, as members relate to each other's issues.
- Action learning groups – promote reflection on practice-based issues using group support that focuses on self-directed individual actions (see *Table 3.2*).

- NHS employers offer regular corporate communication events, staff conversation groups or discussion forums open to all employees to discuss global initiatives and make you aware of local opportunities. Check emails and local intranet sites for future dates.
- There are many national professional networks and online forums that you can join to keep up to date with the latest career opportunities. The Royal College of Nursing (RCN) and Royal College of Midwives (RCM) have a wide range of professional forums and networks that are excellent and free to join.

## 2.3 TRAINING, EDUCATION AND PROFESSIONAL DEVELOPMENT

### 2.3.1 Statutory and mandatory training

- Statutory training is the training which an employer is legally required to provide. For example, statutory 'Equality and Diversity' training is essential for all staff that must adhere to the 2010 Equality Act. It is important that you complete all statutory training, prior to working in any area, as you may not be fully covered by insurers to practise without this training.
- Mandatory training is an organisational requirement to limit risk and maintain safe working practice. Mandatory training is based on your responsibilities and job description, as opposed to UK laws. The organisation decides what is essential for its staff to practise safely, and such training will be role-specific, e.g. conflict resolution training for RNs in a hospital.

Healthcare providers often use the terms 'compulsory' or 'essential' training interchangeably, to cover both statutory and mandatory training.

## Statutory training

The minimum statutory training requirements for all levels of nurses, theatre staff and midwives usually include the following areas:
- Fire safety
- Equality and diversity
- Health and safety
- Control of Substances Hazardous to Health (COSHH) regulations
- Reporting of Injuries, Diseases and Dangerous Occurrences Regulations (RIDDOR)
- Information governance
- Manual handling.

## Mandatory training

Always check with your line manager which specific mandatory training is required as part of your specific role. A selection of mandatory training from a variety of fields is presented below:
- Adult/children/neonatal hospital life support
- Anaphylaxis training
- Blood glucose monitoring
- Blood safety and safe blood transfusion
- Child protection and safeguarding children
- Clinical record-keeping
- Complaints handling
- Conflict resolution
- Consent and mental capacity
- Electronic patient records
- Insulin administration
- Infection prevention and control
- Safeguarding adults
- Abuse, neglect and exploitation
- Medical devices
- Venous thromboembolism (VTE) prevention
- Maternal and fetal/neonatal assessment/escalation tools
- Antepartum and postpartum haemorrhage
- Vaginal breech management
- Perineal trauma, repair and care.

Your first training priority when starting any role will be to complete statutory and mandatory training. Statutory/mandatory training will remain ongoing throughout your career, as some training expires annually and will need repeating to keep in date.

### 2.3.2 NHS staff passport system

NHS England (2019) has recently introduced a new NHS staff passport system for healthcare professionals, designed to make it easier for staff to move between Trusts and new roles across sites. Hospitals are being encouraged to sign up to the new system, which aims to decrease the amount of pre-employment checks, inductions, mandatory training and appraisals. It is envisaged that staff will take their NHS passport with them wherever they work in the future, and that it will contain all previous learning and professional development documentation.

### 2.3.3 Induction and orientation to a new role

Whenever you start a new role you should have a specified period of induction and an orientation to your practice setting and/or role, which should include supernumerary time. Supernumerary time, where your presence at work is not counted in the rota numbers, allows you time to complete essential training and to familiarise yourself with the area. Experienced staff appointed to a new position should also receive supernumerary time, as they need to acclimatise to their new responsibilities.

There is variety in the amount of supernumerary time awarded across clinical settings, ranging from a few days to several weeks, or months in some intensive care units. Your employer is not obliged to give you supernumerary time to complete induction and statutory/mandatory training. However, most managers allocate a number of study days, and it is helpful to find out how much supernumerary time will be offered to you before you commence any post.

The structure and content of orientation programmes for staff across the UK may range from a few pages of local information to an in-depth competency-based orientation as part of a year-long training programme. It is important that you determine what is expected of you during any orientation period, along with time frames for completion. *Table 2.1* is an example of a comprehensive orientation checklist identifying key information that you can adapt to suit your own learning and development needs.

*Table 2.1:* Orientation checklist

| Key areas | Specific information | Completed |
|---|---|---|
| 1. Statutory/ mandatory training | • List of statutory/mandatory training<br>• Training booking system and how to navigate<br>• Electronic learning management system to access workbooks/eLearning | |
| 2. Roles and responsibilities | • Job description, personal specifications and new role requirements<br>• List of roles within the team and responsibilities<br>• List of roles within the allied health professions and responsibilities<br>• Organisational structures and hierarchy within the institution, Trust or community setting<br>• System for allocation and delegation of caseloads<br><br>Additional responsibilities for experienced staff/managers:<br>• Budgeting<br>• Maintaining staffing establishments, doing rotas and planning future projections<br>• Maintaining performance standards, local auditing and reporting data following incidents<br>• Operational and strategic management relevant to role | |
| 3. Policies | • Location of national and local policies/standards<br>• Policy to book rota requests, study days, annual/ compassionate leave<br><br>Additional policies for management position:<br>• Managing staff sickness absence and return to work interviews<br>• Managing staff performance<br>• Preventing and managing clinical risks<br>• Managing bullying and harassment at work<br>• Managing emergencies and on-call duties | |
| 4. Documentation | • Documentation required for patient pathways (admission to discharge)<br>• Patient documentation: observation charts, pre-op checklists, consent forms<br>• Acuity and dependency tools<br>• Paperwork less frequently used, e.g. self-discharge, Deprivation of Liberty, registering death, storing valuables, assessing mental capacity and Do not attempt cardiopulmonary resuscitation (DNACPR) forms<br>• Systems to document care, e.g. electronic patient records (EPR)<br>• Standardised care plans<br><br>Additional documentation if management position:<br>• Local budgets and future financial projections<br>• Current and predicted staffing establishments/ rosters | |

*Table 2.1: (continued)*

| Key areas | Specific Information | Completed |
|---|---|---|
| | • Previous CQC reports<br>• Clinical incident reports and clinical governance reports<br>• Past and current staff performance issues<br>• Strategic operational plans | |
| 5. Risk assessments | • National and local risk assessment documentation<br><br>Additional information if management position:<br>• Previous clinical risk assessments, action plans/outcomes and any serious incidents requiring investigation (SIRIs) | |
| 6. Human Resources (HR) | • HR team roles and responsibilities<br>• Location of HR department | |
| 7. Orientating to the service | • Layout of the setting (or region if community role)<br>• Electronic systems used as part of the role<br>• Position of setting relative to other healthcare providers or key staff<br>• Type of handovers, e.g. patient bedside handover, written, tape recorded, MDT<br>• Location of handover, emergency equipment and fire exits<br>• Security in the clinical/community setting, e.g. security codes, safety bleeps/personal alarm<br>• Storage of patient notes<br>• Type of nursing organisational system used, e.g. primary nursing<br>• Key telephone numbers/contacts, e.g. specialist nurses and line managers<br>• Referral system to doctors and allied health professionals<br>• Patient call bell system<br>• Shift patterns and breaks<br>• System for reporting sickness | |
| 8. Bleeping and escalation | • National Early Warning scoring system and escalation policy<br>• Escalation system relating to poor care<br><br>Additional information if management position:<br>• bleep and on-call responsibilities and future on-call rotas<br>• system for support and advice when you are on call | |
| 9. Incident reporting | • System to report incidents and escalate concerns<br>• Procedure for preventing and reporting injury, e.g. a needle-stick injury<br><br>Additional information if management position:<br>• roles and responsibilities for reporting on and learning from incidents | |

*Table 2.1: (continued)*

| Key areas | Specific information | Completed |
|---|---|---|
| 10. Medication and pharmacy | • Common medications used in the setting, their actions/side-effects<br>• Location of pharmacy/pharmacist<br>• System to contact pharmacist (normal hours/out of hours)<br>• Controlled drug and medication storage<br>• Medication ordering and prescribing<br>• Drug administration policy and procedure for reporting drug error<br>• Patient self-administration medication policy (if appropriate) | |
| 11. Equipment training | • List of equipment used and where stored/cleaned/maintained<br>• How to use equipment and training required | |
| 12. Patient information | • Types of patients and common conditions<br>• Usual patient pathways<br>• Patient information packs<br><br>Additional information if management position:<br>• Previous patient experience/satisfaction feedback and survey data and actions | |
| 13. Competencies and training | • Induction programme<br>• Orientation/preceptorship period and how delivered<br>• Person signing you off as competent in your new role<br>• System to professionally review your practice over next 12 months, e.g. observational/reflective<br>• Role-specific skills required and training, e.g. role-specific competencies/objectives/leadership frameworks<br>• Support systems offered | |

NOTE: *The information in this table is to be used ONLY as an example and may require changes/additions/deletions, according to your service.*

### 2.3.4 Preceptorship

The Department of Health (DH, 2010), Nursing and Midwifery Council (NMC, 2008) and Royal College of Midwives (RCM, 2017) advise that all NQNs/NQMs should have a period of structured preceptorship on qualification. During the preceptorship period, the NQN/NQM (the 'preceptee') will be supported by one trained nurse/midwife (their 'preceptor') within their clinical setting. In reality, it is not always feasible for an NQN/NQM to be able to work every shift with their preceptor over the full preceptorship period. If preceptors are not available, shift 'buddies' or practice supervisors may be allocated, to provide assurance that there is a trained professional available for support. NQNs/NQMs are expected to observe experienced staff to increase their knowledge while learning on the job during their preceptorship period.

There is no mandatory requirement for employers to deliver preceptorship, as it is only "strongly recommended" by the NMC (2008) and the RCM (2017). The NMC does not monitor the implementation of preceptorship across the UK, leading to widespread differences in its implementation. The preceptorship period may last anything from three months to one year post-qualification. Understandably, the implementation of preceptorship has been found to be variable across the UK as a result of staff shortages and service demands. However, a more consistent approach to preceptorship is found in Scotland. In 2017, the Scottish Government became the first UK regional government to support the NHS Education for Scotland (NES) Flying Start NHS programme.

A number of key terms relating to the implementation of preceptorship are presented in *Table 2.2*. A form to guide feedback from your preceptor, or shift buddy, is presented in *Figure 2.1*.

*Table 2.2: Terms, definitions and guidance relating to preceptorship*

| Terms | Definitions and guidance |
|---|---|
| Preceptorship | • A structured period of transition for a newly registered practitioner where they are supported by a preceptor, to develop their confidence and skills in practice, as part of their lifelong learning<br>• Preceptorship involves a preceptor supporting a preceptee in their clinical setting by providing an opportunity to reflect on practice, receive constructive feedback and have access to relevant post-registration learning<br>• Preceptorship should be guided by role-specific competencies and a personalised development programme |
| Preceptorship period | • The initial period after registration, and during a preceptee's first appointment as a qualified nurse/midwife, is referred to as the preceptorship period<br>• There is no standard time frame for the preceptorship period and it can range from a few months to a year; the NMC (2008) and DH (2010) advise that the preceptorship period should last up to one year |
| Preceptee | • A preceptee is an NQN/NQM or allied health professional who is allocated a preceptor to support their development in a practice setting; from the first day of their appointment a preceptee should be allocated a named preceptor |
| Preceptor | • A preceptor is a named member of qualified staff who is allocated to support a preceptee's development during their preceptorship period, usually up to a year<br>• The preceptor must be based in the clinical setting, have been qualified for at least a year and have experience of supervising others<br>• The preceptor does not have to have a qualification, but must have good knowledge of the area<br>• The preceptor is responsible for providing a newly qualified nurse with structured support in clinical practice during their preceptorship period |

| PRECEPTORSHIP PRACTICE FEEDBACK FORM FOR NEWLY QUALIFIED NURSE/MIDWIFE | |
|---|---|
| Name of preceptee: | |
| Name of preceptor/shift mentor: | |
| Date and time of shift: | |
| Is the preceptee supernumerary on shift: YES/NO (please circle) | |
| Ward area/community setting/clinical setting: | |
| Overall aim(s) for feedback on the shift | *(e.g. to develop the nurse's/midwife's time management skills when caring for a caseload)* |
| Detail your previous experience and the feedback you will find helpful during your shift | *(Detail how long you have been qualified, and feedback that would help your development)* |

**Figure 2.1:** *(continued)*

Following your shift, please reflect on what you did well and areas you need to work on.
Detail additional support that will help improve your practice:

Preceptor/shift supervisor: please give feedback on the nurse's/midwife's performance during the shift, detailing what they did well and what their strengths are:

Please summarise/bullet point key areas to work on in the future using joint goal planning:

Please detail additional support/training that you have suggested that may develop the nurse/midwife in the future:

| Preceptee's signature: | | Date: | |
| Preceptor/supervisor's signature: | | Date: | |

*Figure 2.1: Practice feedback form for newly qualified nurse/midwife.*

### 2.3.5 The NHS Leadership Academy

The NHS Leadership Academy supports a variety of national leadership programmes aimed at healthcare staff aspiring to leadership roles. Several courses are available, including:

- the Edward Jenner programme: a free eLearning programme aimed at new leaders who wish to gain a fresh perspective on the delivery of services and the impact on patient experiences. On completion of the programme individuals are awarded an NHS Leadership Academy Award in Leadership Foundations. This award provides a first step towards the Mary Seacole programme.
- the Mary Seacole programme: aimed at individuals who are looking to move into their first leadership role or are new to leadership. On completion of the programme individuals are awarded an NHS Leadership Academy Award in Healthcare Leadership.
- the Rosalind Franklin programme: aimed at mid-level leaders aspiring to lead large and complex programmes, departments, services or systems of care. On completion of the programme individuals are awarded an NHS Leadership Academy Award in Senior Healthcare Leadership.
- the Elizabeth Garrett Anderson programme: aimed at mid-level leaders with the confidence to drive lasting change and improve patient experience. On completion of the programme individuals are awarded an NHS Leadership Academy Award in Senior Healthcare Leadership and an MSc in Healthcare Leadership.
- the Nye Bevan programme: aimed at senior leaders who wish to progress into executive roles and improve performance at board level. On completion of the programme individuals are awarded an NHS Leadership Academy Award in Executive Healthcare Leadership.
- the Ready Now programme: aimed at senior black, Asian or minority ethnic (BAME) leaders working in the NHS or providing NHS-funded services (in England) at a band 8a or above and aspiring to a board level position.

See the NHS Leadership Academy online resources:
www.leadershipacademy.nhs.uk

### 2.3.6 Different levels and credits for university modules and courses

Professional education does not always require a university level course and there may be excellent in-house study days and conferences that you can access for free. If you choose to undertake university study, the following questions will help guide discussions with your manager:

1. What modules/courses are available and suitable for my future development?
2. What level of study is required and what credits are awarded?
3. How do I apply for modules/courses?
4. Who funds modules/courses and supports study leave in my area?
5. How can I apply for module/course funding and study leave if required?

**KEY TIP**

- Regular PDRs with your line manager and advice from experienced practitioners will enable you to decide which in-house and external courses are most suitable for your needs (see *Section 2.4*).

## University courses and the credit system

When reviewing future university courses, you need an understanding of the credit levels assigned to different programmes and modules. UK universities use the Quality Assurance Agency for Higher Education (QAA) (2009) credit system (see *Table 2.3*).

*Table 2.3: QAA credit system*

| Type of course | Credit level | Total credits |
|---|---|---|
| Doctorate (PhD/DPhil) | Level 8 | 540 credits |
| Master's | Level 7 | 480 credits |
| Degree (BA/BSc) | Level 6 | 360 credits |
| Foundation degree | Level 5 | 240 credits |
| Apprenticeship | Level 3 | 120 credits |

*NOTE: Credits may vary across certain university courses.*

## Building blocks

Your module credits are accumulated, like building blocks, until you achieve the total credit required for the final academic qualification. You should contact individual universities to establish what the requirements are for any specific programmes you are interested in.

Modules are classed as single or double/treble and the amount of credits awarded vary accordingly.

- Credits awarded on 1 × double module = the credits awarded on 2 × single modules.

### Accreditation of Prior Experiential Learning (APEL) system

The QAA credit system allows you to accrue credits that may be required on another course; for example, the first year of a BSc (Hons) degree may be used to transfer to the second year on another degree. Nurses from overseas may wish to have previous post-qualification courses accredited from outside the UK. UK universities can use the APEL system, which is recognised internationally. The learner usually requires a transcript from their previous university, an academic statement from a personal tutor for verification, and example work to demonstrate they have covered the module content required to cover the APEL requested.

### Time required in notional hours

The amount of learning indicated by a credit value on a module or course is based on the total number of notional hours of learning. The number of notional hours of learning provides a guide as to how long it will take an average student to achieve the module/course outcomes. Within the UK, one credit represents 10 notional hours of learning:

- On one module 150 notional hours of learning = 15 credits.

### 2.3.7 How do I secure funding and study leave for my course?

You may have clear career goals; however, you cannot presume your line manager will support a request for paid study leave to attend university every week or offer financial support to cover tuition fees. Accessing course funding and receiving paid study time is increasingly competitive and managers may ask staff to attend an interview prior to allocating funding. To give yourself the best chance of success you need to demonstrate how you have positively supported others and influenced change in your current role (see *Step 3*), and spend time preparing for future applications and interviews (see *Steps 4* and *5*).

Alternatively, you can self-fund modules and complete coursework in your own time. Always ask your manager if you are entitled to any paid study leave first. Most employers will have a study leave policy that defines the maximum amount of study days that a staff member can receive in any given year.

Managers can allow staff to use their day off or annual leave to attend university. However, they may refuse a request if there is a risk to their service; e.g. you are the only person available to run a GP clinic every Monday. Prior to self-funding courses, always check that your manager will support your attendance on the set study day. The alternative to taught study is flexible online or distance learning modules/courses, which are self-directed. Distance learning course content is web-based and therefore can be completed anywhere that suits you, in your own time.

## 2.4 PROFESSIONAL DEVELOPMENT REVIEWS (PDRS)

During your career you will require ongoing regular feedback on your practical skills and knowledge, which will inform your future Professional Development Plans (PDPs) and PDRs. Your line manager, preceptor or clinical supervisor may complete your professional reviews. A few questions are presented below to help guide your future reviews:

- Who will be conducting my PDR?
- What are their contact details and how do I arrange to meet them?
- How often should I meet my reviewer over the next year?
- What do they expect from me?
- What support, guidance and feedback will they offer me?
- How will they document my reviews?
- Where can I find additional resources to support my PDR and future PDP?

When you first start in a role you should ideally have a PDR at 3, 6, 9 and 12 months, which will lead to a 12-month annual appraisal. After you are established in a role, you should negotiate regular reviews, as and when needed. PDRs are based on evaluating your learning goals, objectives or role-specific competencies. Following your review, new goals will be set and a future review date will be planned. You should discuss any specific learning needs and training opportunities during your review to inform your future career progression.

### 2.4.1 What is a developmental aim and how does it differ from a learning objective?

There is usually one overall teaching, training or development aim (think of it as one strategy), whereas there will be a number of objectives (things to do) to complete the aim. The aim is usually an overall statement of intent that relates to specific objectives or goals set. Learning objectives (sometimes called learning outcomes) are statements that describe what you need to be able to do as a result of your learning.

Aims will include general words such as 'know', 'understand', 'use' or 'show', whereas objectives will use 'active verbs' to demonstrate their achievement, such as 'list', 'state', 'explain', 'discuss' or 'describe'. *Figure 2.2* contains some verbs associated with knowledge, skills and attitudes that may be used within your future learning objectives, and *Figure 2.3* provides an example aim and objectives.

| Overall aim | Example verbs for your learning objectives |
|---|---|
| KNOWLEDGE: to be able to demonstrate increased knowledge and understanding of… | Identify, define, state, interpret, list, label, classify, outline, record, evaluate, compare, recognise, calculate, label |
| SKILL: to be able to competently… | Use, locate, employ, maintain, measure, observe, chart, establish, interact, modify |
| ATTITUDES: to be able to demonstrate attitudes or values that reflect… | Value, support, consider, evaluate, challenge, characterise |

*Figure 2.2: Example of verbs to use in learning objectives.*

| Aim | Objectives (verbs in **bold**) |
|---|---|
| To understand the roles and responsibilities of allied health professionals | • **Review** my job description and **identify** my key role and responsibilities as a band …………………….…<br>• **List** all allied health professional roles related to my clinical area<br>• **Compare** roles and responsibilities of allied health professionals and **outline** how they relate to, or differ from mine<br>• **List** key allied health professional leads to contact and **book** one-to-one meeting with them during my supernumerary time<br>• **Describe** how each role may affect patient care and the service in which I work<br>• **Write** a reflection on what I have learnt from my visits to other allied health professionals |

*Figure 2.3: Example aim and objectives for a nurse/midwife.*

### 2.4.2 What is a SMART goal and how do I write one?

The widely used acronym SMART can help you set learning goals that can be measured, and their achievement will demonstrate your progression in practice development plans. SMART goals should be:
• Specific
• Measurable
• Achievable
• Realistic
• Time-based.

Details linked to each element of the acronym are presented in *Figure 2.4.*

| Elements of the SMART acronym | Details |
|---|---|
| **S**pecific | • Goal is specific and significant to your learning and development<br>• Goal is clear to understand, concise and well defined |
| **M**easurable | • Goal is quantifiable to allow you to measure the outcome when completed<br>• Goal has an established benchmark for measuring |
| **A**chievable | • Goal is achievable and accessible<br>• Goal is based on your skill and resources<br>• Goal is based in your area of practice<br>• Goal is action-orientated, containing an action verb<br>• Goals should be agreed between you and your preceptor |
| **R**ealistic | • Goal should be realistic, relevant and applicable to your practice role<br>• Goal should be achieved within available resources and time |
| **T**ime-based | • Goal should have specific timelines attached, along with a feasible deadline for completion of goals<br>• There should be enough time to complete the goal |

*Figure 2.4: SMART acronyms and details.*

Example stages to help you write a SMART goal are presented in *Figure 2.5.*

**Stage 1:** Start by just identifying what you want to learn:

*"I want to learn about different allied health professional roles in my new community setting."*

**Stage 2:** Be specific and try to write it down in one sentence. Remember to be clear and concise and not use a vague phrase like *"I want..."*, as you will not know when you have reached your goal:

*"To increase my understanding of different allied health professional roles and their role responsibilities in my new community setting."*

**Stage 3:** Use an action verb to describe what you want to achieve and to make the goal measurable:

*"To increase my understanding of different allied health professional (AHP) roles and staff responsibilities in my community setting, by identifying all relevant AHP roles and determining how each role is responsible for patient and service delivery in my community setting."*

**Stage 4:** Link the goal to your specific practice with timelines for achievement and completion:

*"Within 1 month, I will identify all relevant allied health professional (AHP) roles within my community setting and determine the responsibilities related to each AHP role and the effect these roles have on patient care and service delivery."*

**Stage 5:** Add how you will show you have completed the goal and then you have your SMART goal! Once written, you can always check whether your goal is Specific, Measurable, Achievable, Realistic and Time-based.

*Figure 2.5: (continued)*

---

**SMART GOAL:**

*"Within one month, my preceptor will assess that I have the required level of knowledge and understanding of all allied health professional (AHP) roles and staff responsibilities within my community setting, and the effect these roles have on patient care and delivery."*

Examples of evidence to demonstrate completion of SMART goal:

- In one month, my preceptor will question my knowledge and understanding of each AHP role in my community setting and how each role affects patient care and delivery.
- My preceptor will review my reflective accounts detailing what I have learnt from each of my visits and observations with our community AHPs.
- My preceptor will review my competence and sign off my competency statement: *"having the required level of knowledge and understanding of AHP roles in the community setting and their effect on patient care and service delivery".*

---

*Figure 2.5: Stages to help develop and write a SMART goal.*

## 2.4.3  Professional development goals

Following your PDR or an appraisal, you will be tasked with discussing and writing goals/actions relating to your future development (see *Figure 2.6* for simple example development goals relating to different bands).

| Question: How do you plan to professionally develop yourself in the future? |
|---|
| **Band 5** |
| Goal: Within 3 months I will be able to safely administer IV medications to patients. |
| How will you achieve this goal? |
| 1. I will attend our mandatory IV training day and practical skills sessions for NQNs/NQMs. |
| 2. I will review all related policies and guidelines, such as: preparing and administering injectables; aseptic non-touch technique (ANTT) and infection control policies. |
| 3. I will complete and pass all statutory eLearning modules relating to the administration of injectables, infection control and administration of blood and blood components. |
| 4. I will be observed a minimum of 10 times administering IV medications under the direct supervision of my preceptor. Following 10 observations, I may request more practice observations if I do not feel confident in my abilities, or my preceptor feels I require more practice. |
| 5. I will receive a final sign-off from my preceptor when assessed as competent to administer IVs independently. |
| How will you know you have met this goal? |
| • I will be signed off as competent by my preceptor and able to competently administer IV medications independently. |
| **Band 6** |
| Goal: Within 2 months I will be able to complete the e-roster for our community team. |
| How will you achieve this goal? |
| 1. I will attend a practical electronic e-roster lunchtime training session to learn how to navigate our e-roster system. |
| 2. I will review safe staffing establishments to increase my knowledge of safe staffing. |
| 3. I will observe my manager using the e-roster system over a 2-week period. |
| 4. I will book admin days with my manager to have e-roster slots together. |
| 5. I will do my first e-roster whilst being supervised by my manager. |
| 6. I will receive feedback on future e-rosters that will be signed off by my manager, until I feel confident enough to complete e-rosters independently. |

*Figure 2.6: (continued)*

How will you know you have met this goal?
- I will be able to complete e-rosters independently that are authorised for release.

**Band 7**

Goal: Within 6 months I will complete my first master's module for my leadership course.

How will you achieve this goal?
1. I will attend the master's programme study day every Wednesday and ensure that the unit is managed by my deputies during my study days.
2. I will meet my university supervisor every month to gain feedback on my assignment draft work.
3. I will attend a study skills training session to improve the level of my academic writing.
4. I will attend a librarian session on how to use EndNote software tool to better manage my bibliography, citations and references.

How will you know you have met this goal?
- I will successfully pass my master's module.

*Figure 2.6: Example development goals.*

# 2.5 APPRAISALS

An 'appraisal' is the act of making a judgement about somebody or something. Healthcare regulators, such as the CQC and Department of Health, advocate that all healthcare employers should provide an annual appraisal for their staff, as it is deemed essential to promoting high quality care (DH, 2004; Department of Health, Social Services and Public Safety, 2015). As part of your ongoing development, you should be offered an annual appraisal by your line manager for the rest of your career.

The person conducting your appraisal is called an appraiser and you are the appraisee. Once you secure a date for an annual appraisal, you should prepare well in advance to gain the best out of it. An appraisal is a chance for you to receive constructive feedback and support from your manager to enable you to become the best you can in your role. An appraisal is not the correct place for a manager to deal with disciplinary procedures.

## 2.5.1 *How is an appraisal structured?*

UK employers use a variety of frameworks and headings on appraisal documentation such as:
- NHS Knowledge and Skills Framework (KSF)
- NMC *Code* (2018a) themes
- competency frameworks or job descriptors
- local frameworks aligned to quality priorities.

Aim to become familiar with appraisal frameworks within your local area, which are usually online. Appraisals should remain confidential at all times and be conducted in a private room. An annual appraisal usually covers the following areas:

- How your role relates to the rest of the team/organisation
- Personal and professional development over the last year
- Your current knowledge and skills in line with requirements for the role
- Your current competence and performance using a job description and/or competencies
- Your achievements using previously set role-specific objectives/ development goals
- Education and training opportunities available over the next year
- Additional support you may access over the next year
- Future career progression and options to develop within your current role
- Setting future objectives and priorities as part of your personal development plan.

### 2.5.2  How to make the most of your appraisal

Further tips to inform your future appraisals are presented below:

**Before your appraisal**

- Be proactive:
    - proactively book your appraisal well in advance of your due date and check how your appraiser prefers you to book them, e.g. email, verbally or calendar invitation.
- Don't worry:
    - there is no need to worry before an appraisal, as your appraiser should lead you through local structures.
- Familiarise yourself with the appraisal template:
    - review your appraisal template before your meeting
    - usually there will be two comment boxes, one for you and one for your appraiser, to write/type the following:
        1. How you have progressed relating to your job descriptors or previous objectives/goals
        2. How your current role relates to your team
        3. What has been achieved by you since the last appraisal
        4. What additional support or training opportunities will help you progress
        5. What your objectives/development plans are for next year.

- Find out what your line manager expects you to prepare:
    - prior to your appraisal, write notes on the areas 1–5 above and check what measures your appraiser will use to evaluate your progression
    - some appraisers are happy to chat through progression with limited preparation; others will request evidence of achievement.

## During your appraisal

- Make your own notes:
    - it is easy to forget what has been discussed in an appraisal; you may make notes during your meeting or complete an online appraisal template as you go along or afterwards.
- Consider your performance:
    - your appraiser will review your personal qualities and competence using key measures such as: band 5 competencies and development goals.
    - consider your achievements over the previous year using related measures to summarise your progression.
- Communication should be two-way:
    - two-way communication is an essential part of an appraisal; you should have the opportunity to give your perspective and discuss areas where you require extra support
    - you may not achieve previously set goals due to a lack of opportunity or support; an appraisal is an appropriate forum for you to discuss reasons for this.
- Use constructive feedback to inform your future practice:
    - managers should be trained to appraise staff and give constructive feedback; you, in turn, need to listen and receive feedback to develop your future knowledge and skills
    - if you do not agree with appraisal feedback, then constructively state why; offer your appraiser factual examples to demonstrate your points and support your perspective.
- Acknowledge personal issues:
    - we all have lives outside work and sometime personal issues such as a divorce, bereavement or ill health may impact on our performance; most managers are experienced at supporting staff through difficult times
    - if you are struggling, you may wish to discuss personal issues as part of your appraisal; however, you do not have to if it makes you uncomfortable.

### Appraisal documentation

- Setting objectives and personal development plans for the next year:
  - following your appraisal, new objectives and goals are set for completion over the next year
  - personal development plans will need to be updated with new review dates
  - opportunities for additional training and support should be included in your plans.
- Complete sign-off:
  - once all sections within your appraisal form are complete, your appraisal can be signed off by both you and your appraiser
  - signing off your appraisal indicates that you have both read the content and reviewed the other person's views
  - never sign off your appraisal without stating your view in the comments section; if you are unhappy with the comments from your appraiser, then ensure that your perspective is documented.

 **KEY TIP**

- Make the most of your appraisal by preparing thoroughly in advance.

### 2.5.3 Dealing with disciplinary procedures

If your line manager informs you that you are not progressing well, they should do this in a supportive, constructive and professional manner, i.e. not in earshot of patients or other staff. The staff member should be respected and all discussion relating to concerns should take place in a private and confidential environment. Your line manager should be explicit as to what you need to improve on and how they will support you to achieve a positive outcome.

If you are deemed to be underperforming in your role, your manager should deal with performance issues according to local procedures, e.g. Managing Work Performance Procedure. Managing staff performance should initially focus on supporting the employee to help them improve their performance to meet the standard required.

Most contracts contain a probationary period of 3–6 months, to provide a safety net for employers after they have recruited you. The probationary period is when your ability to perform at the required level is observed and assessed. If you fail to achieve the standard within the probationary period, employers can potentially dismiss you without concerns of unfair dismissal and employment tribunals later. If you are unsure of procedures, or concerned about the way you are being supported, talk to your local HR department.

During an informal stage you should be offered the following:

- An initial meeting with your manager, who should:
  - state what they expect from you
  - detail the specific area(s) of your practice you need to improve on
  - provide details of how progress will be measured, e.g. competency achievement
  - propose a future plan of support to help improve your performance
  - give you an opportunity to discuss your perspective of the situation
  - provide a copy of documentation from the meeting for your records.
- A Performance Improvement Plan (PIP): a PIP should be written which clearly sets out the areas of concern, objectives or goals to be achieved, how success (the outcome) will be measured, and the timescales.
- Future progress review meetings: you should be made aware of future progress review meetings in advance, along with who is attending and reviewing your progress. Often managers will oversee a PIP and lead a review meeting, but will expect a team leader/educator to sign off goals or competencies.
- Documentation: you should receive a copy of your PIP documentation, review meetings and any related objectives/competencies/goals, for the duration. There should always be space on review documentation for you to write your perspective of the situation and whether you are happy/unhappy with the support offered, or find any aspects of the process difficult. Although you are not being formally performance-managed at this stage, records from an informal discussion can remain on a person's file for 6 months.
- Additional support/training: your individual learning needs should be reviewed and additional support offered to help you achieve set objectives/goals.

The majority of staff who complete a PIP have fulfilling careers with no further performance issues. However, you should be aware that if you are assessed as not improving with additional PIP support, your employer could move to a formal disciplinary stage. Local disciplinary procedures usually contain a flow chart that includes the following stages:

- Informal meeting
- PIP review meetings
- First formal meeting (written warning)
- Second formal meeting (final written warning)
- Formal performance hearing (potential dismissal)
- Appeals meeting.

(Always check the details of local procedures: 'Managing Work Performance Procedure' or 'Disciplinary Procedure'.)

Following any formal actions it is important that you take independent legal advice, which is covered by your Union subscriptions.

NOTE: never work in practice without Union cover as this provides full indemnity cover and legal advice/representation when you need it.

Following cases of gross misconduct, such as violence towards a patient, an employee can be 'dismissed with immediate effect' and without notice or payment.

## 2.6 THE IMPORTANCE OF NMC REGISTRATION AND REVALIDATION

When you complete a nursing/midwifery degree, you will be directed by the university programme lead to complete paperwork applying for your first NMC registration, as an RN/RM. You are required to pay annual NMC fees to register and receive a personal NMC PIN. Your first employer will request evidence of an active NMC PIN before you sign a formal employment contract, which means you must register with the NMC prior to starting your first post.

Throughout the rest of your career you are required to:
- pay an annual NMC fee to remain on the NMC register
- complete an NMC online process called revalidation every three years, to maintain your NMC registration.

It is the registrant's responsibility to pay annual registration fees and revalidate every three years before NMC expiry dates are due. To ensure that your registration does not lapse, you must register with NMC Online and actively check that fee payments go through on time. Your NMC registration will lapse and your NMC account will be deemed 'inactive' if fees are not paid or you do not complete your revalidation on time.

It is illegal to work as an RN or RM (in any circumstances) if you are unregistered. NMC Online sends you a reminder when fees are due or your registration is near to lapsing (currently sent 60 days before expiry or revalidation date). It is important to inform the NMC of any changes to your home/email addresses, in order to receive these vital reminders.

### 2.6.1 *What happens if my NMC registration lapses by accident?*

Reputable healthcare employers will not accept reasons for lapses in NMC registration, as you are essentially working illegally as an RN/RM. You are accountable and responsible for registering with NMC Online and can view your account to ascertain fee and revalidation expiry dates. If you allow your NMC registration to expire, your employer will usually stop payment of your wages (including maternity/sick pay) for all 'unregistered' days, which includes any days off. All of which gives you a good incentive to keep in date!

If you suddenly realise that your NMC registration has expired and you are at work, you must stop working immediately and inform your line manager that you have a lapsed registration. This is dealt with formally and line managers should request that you leave the clinical setting immediately (Chu and Giles, 2019). Employers usually start a 'disciplinary procedure' as your absence will affect staffing and impact on service provision, and your insurance at work is invalid without registration. If you receive a first formal letter from your employer, it must be highlighted on future references. Following a lapse in registration, it can take 2–6 weeks to rectify through the NMC readmission process (NMC, 2019). If you are found to be working unregistered, your application may be referred to the NMC's Investigating Committee panel; for example, if you knowingly worked as an RN/RM for a long period without registration.

In summary, don't ever let your NMC registration lapse!

### 2.6.2  How do I revalidate every three years?

Since April 2016, an NMC revalidation process must be followed by all RNs/RMs every three years to maintain their NMC registration (NMC, 2018d). If it is your first time revalidating, do not worry as most employers are used to the process.

**KEY TIPS**

- Aim to maintain continuous CPD records, practice feedback and written reflections, so you are not pulling documentation together immediately before your NMC revalidation date.
- Maintain an ongoing professional portfolio to record and store documentation for your NMC revalidation (see *Professional portfolios, Section 4.5*).
- Ask experienced staff in your local area about the process, as they should be used to acting as 'Confirmers' and can talk you through the process, well in advance of your revalidation due date.

Further tips:
- Ensure that your revalidation is completed by the first day of the month in which your registration expires.
- The revalidation process requires someone to act as a 'Confirmer', usually your line manager, to verify that you have the required number of practice hours and evidence of continuous practice development (see *Table 2.4*). It is helpful to identify who your NMC Confirmer is, to chat through the process.
- Plan your revalidation review well in advance as managers can be busy (as early as 6 months before your revalidation due date).
- Prepare your revalidation evidence prior to the meeting, to make the process as easy as possible for your Confirmer.
- Ensure that you review current NMC revalidation processes, forms, templates and resources prior to your revalidation, as they are very helpful (NMC, 2018d).
- You must register with NMC Online to complete your revalidation form, which verifies you have met with your Confirmer and have met the criteria required to revalidate.

*Table 2.4:* NMC requirements for revalidation every three years (NMC, 2018d)

| NMC requirements | Evidence and examples |
|---|---|
| Practice hours over the last three years | • A minimum of 450 hours if already registered with NMC (900 hours if renewing registration)<br>• Usually your manager will have access to e-rosters demonstrating your practice hours |
| Continuous Practice Development (CPD) | • 35 hours of CPD (20 hours must be participatory learning)<br>• Participatory learning includes any learning activity where you interact with other people, e.g. study group, conference or group forum on a virtual environment<br>• You must demonstrate accurate records of your CPD recorded in hours and the types of development, e.g. records on your eLearning account, competencies achieved, certificates from completed academic and professional courses, study days or course workbooks<br>• You must demonstrate how you have related your CPD to practice, which can be verbally discussed or written notes<br>• NMC (2018d) templates are helpful<br>• Do not include personal data on revalidation documents |
| Practice-related feedback | • Five accounts of practice-related feedback<br>• A range of practice-related feedback can be used, such as patient thank you cards, feedback from colleagues, evaluations from others you have mentored or teaching evaluations |

*Table 2.4: (continued)*

| NMC requirements | Evidence and examples |
|---|---|
| Reflective accounts | • Five written reflective accounts<br>• Use a familiar reflective tool to demonstrate what you have learnt and how this has influenced your practice<br>• You may reflect on situations that went well or where you learned from a difficult situation; a simple reflection linked to an element of patient care or your practice is ideal<br>• Reflective accounts can relate to your CPD activity, practice-related feedback or any other event or experience |
| A reflective discussion | • An NMC reflective discussion<br>• A reflective discussion summary must be completed using the correct NMC form (NMC, 2018d) and stored as paper copy |
| | • The reflective discussion record includes:<br>  – name and NMC PIN of the NMC registered RN/RM with whom you had the discussion<br>  – date you had the discussion<br>• If your line manager is not NMC registered, you must discuss your reflective accounts with another NMC registered person |
| Health and character | Making a health and character declaration is completed as part of your online application |
| Professional indemnity | Appropriate indemnity arrangements must be in place, e.g. through a professional body (RCN) or a private insurance arrangement |
| Confirmation | A confirmation form must be signed by your Confirmer (at the end of your revalidation review meeting); you must use the correct NMC (2018d) confirmation form |

## WHAT TO DO NEXT

1. Establish how local educational roles/team structures work and who is responsible for guiding your learning and development in practice.

2. Identify what to expect during your first few months in a post and approach your learning in a structured and methodical way. Write down an orientation checklist list that identifies key information you will need.

3. Identify what statutory and mandatory training you need to complete as your first priority. Statutory and mandatory training remains ongoing throughout your career and will need repeating to keep up to date. You may not be put forward for future development opportunities if your training is out of date.

4. Establish how training and development information is disseminated to staff in your local area. Find out how to navigate local online educational systems to adhere to correct policies and procedures.

5. Establish which assessment and review methods your local area uses to support your development, e.g. annual appraisal, role-specific competencies and PDRs using learning objectives and/or SMART goals.
6. If newly qualified, book 3-, 6-, 9- and 12-month PDRs and establish what preceptorship will be offered during your first year qualified.
7. Establish what professional training and academic courses are available to you locally and nationally, and which courses are funded by your employer. Find out how to formally request and apply for post-registration courses and funding/paid study leave.
8. Establish what processes are used to sign off your NMC revalidation and register with NMC Online. Identify a local NMC Confirmer and prepare your revalidation evidence, such as reflective accounts, over the previous 3 years to make the process as easy as possible.

## REFERENCES AND FURTHER READING

Benner, P. (1984) *From Novice to Expert: excellence and power in clinical nursing practice.* Addison-Wesley Publishing Company.

Chu, C. and Giles, D. (2019) Audit and analysis of lapsed NMC registrations. *MDU journal* (online). Available at: https://mdujournal.themdu.com/issue-archive/spring-2019/audit-and-analysis-of-lapsed-nmc-registrations [accessed 6 December 2019]

Department of Health (2004) *The NHS Knowledge and Skills Framework (NHS KSF) and the Development Review Process* (DH 40440). The Stationery Office.

Department of Health (2010) *Preceptorship Framework for Newly Registered Nurses, Midwives and Allied Health Professionals.* The Stationery Office.

Department of Health, Social Services and Public Safety (2015) *Guidance Notes for Organisations using KSF Development Review/ Appraisal to Support Nurses and Midwives with NMC Revalidation.* Department of Health, Social Services and Public Safety.

Dreyfus, S.E. and Dreyfus, H.L. (1980) *A Five-Stage Model of the Mental Activities Involved in Direct Skill Acquisition* (Supported by the U.S. Airforce, Office of Scientific Research (AFSC)) under contract F49620-C-0063. Unpublished study.

Equality Act (2010) Available at: www.legislation.gov.uk/ukpga/2010/15/contents [accessed 6 December 2019]

Forde-Johnston, C. (2018) *How to Thrive as a Newly Qualified Nurse.* Lantern Publishing.

NHS England (2019) '*NHS Passports' to help staff work flexibly and cut admin costs* (online). Available at: www.england.nhs.uk/2019/09/nhs-passports-to-help-staff-work-flexibly-and-cut-admin-costs/ [accessed 6 December 2019]

Nicholls, S. *et al.* (2000) Clinical governance: its origins and its foundations. *Clinical Performance and Quality Healthcare*, 8(3): 172–8.

Nursing and Midwifery Council (2008a) *Standards to Support Learning and Assessment in Practice: NMC standards for mentors, practice teachers and teachers.* Available at: https://www.nmc.org.uk/global assets/sitedocuments/standards/nmc-standards-to-support-learning-assessment.pdf [accessed 6 December 2019]

Nursing and Midwifery Council (2015) *Guidance on Using Social Media Responsibly.* Available at: https://www.nmc.org.uk/globalassets/sitedocuments/nmc-publications/social-media-guidance.pdf [accessed 6 December 2019]

Nursing and Midwifery Council (2018a) *The Code: professional standards of practice and behaviour for nurses, midwives and nursing associates.* Available at: www.nmc.org.uk/globalassets/sitedocuments/nmc-publications/nmc-code.pdf [accessed 6 December 2019]

Nursing and Midwifery Council (2018b) *Standards of Proficiency for Nursing Associates.* Available at: www.nmc.org.uk/globalassets/site documents/education-standards/nursing-associates-proficiency-standards.pdf [accessed 6 December 2019]

Nursing and Midwifery Council (2018c) *Future Nurse: standards of proficiency for registered nurses.* Available at: www.nmc.org.uk/globalassets/sitedocuments/education-standards/future-nurse-proficiencies.pdf [accessed 6 December 2019]

Nursing and Midwifery Council (2018d) *Revalidation Resources: forms and templates* (online). Available at: http://revalidation.nmc.org.uk/download-resources/forms-and-templates/ [accessed 6 December 2019]

Nursing and Midwifery Council (2019) *Apply for Readmission* (online). Available at: www.nmc.org.uk/registration/returning-to-the-register/readmission/ [accessed 6 December 2019]

The Quality Assurance Agency for Higher Education (2009) *Academic Credit in Higher Education in England: an introduction.* QAA.

Royal College of Nursing (2018) *Careers Resources for Nurses and Midwives* (online). RCN. Available at: www.rcn.org.uk/professional-development/your-career/nurse [accessed 6 December 2019]

Royal College of Midwives (2017) *Position Statement: preceptorship for newly qualified midwives.* RCM. Available at: www.rcm.org.uk/media/2293/preceptorship-for-newly-qualified-midwives.pdf [accessed 6 December 2019]

# STEP 3

# SUPPORT OTHERS AND INFLUENCE CHANGE IN YOUR CURRENT ROLE

*"Be the change you want to see in the world."*
Mahatma Gandhi (1869–1948), Indian political and social
activist who led non-violent resistance campaigns to achieve
India's independence from British rule

## 3.1 WIDEN YOUR PERSPECTIVE AND SUPPORT OTHERS IN YOUR CURRENT ROLE

In our professional role, many of us gain a sense of purpose by enabling others and making a positive difference to individuals and communities. However, healthcare staff must navigate services that are divided into budget-holding businesses, and work across settings with rising numbers of service users and staffing vacancies, all of which increases the risk of a fragmented approach. An overview of workforce issues and future health service delivery plans is presented in (*Section 6.1*). Amidst the current healthcare landscape, a cohesive team approach is more important than ever to support each other's endeavours, nurture colleagues' skills and influence positive changes at work.

Mahatma Gandhi's quote, above, is still regularly cited across the globe to galvanise individuals to stop procrastinating and waiting for others to influence change. Instead, you are called to consider how you can contribute to your wider community and *"be the change you want to see in the world"*. Practical guidance and examples demonstrating how you can positively support others and influence change in your current role are presented throughout this chapter.

Positively contributing to the professional development of others and influencing change within your workplace will help support your future career progression. The practical examples presented within this chapter can be aligned to future career pathways and will strengthen your personal statement, portfolio and CV when applying for future courses or jobs (see *Section 4.1*).

It is important that you have an understanding of frequently used terminology relating to the practical examples presented in this chapter. Key professional terms may also be incorporated into interview questions or as part of a presentation title. A presentation is often requested as part of an interview for a university course place or if you are applying for a band 6 role or above. An overview of key terms is given in *Section 3.4* under the following four headings:

1. Teaching, supervising and supporting others
2. Evidence-based practice and research
3. Improving quality of care
4. Management and leadership.

### 3.1.1 Broaden your perspective and give people a reason to choose you!

It always helps to have a global perspective when planning your career. Many junior staff do not think about the costs to their service when individuals are supported to attend courses. Awarding one band 5 paid study leave to attend a two-module university course, for example, would involve 16 study days (8 study days per module, on average), costing approximately £2000, which comes directly out of your manager's local staffing budget. Additional university course fees will also be required (currently around £1000 per module), which is usually funded from a separate staff education budget. Therefore, prior to a manager investing £4000 towards your annual development, they will, understandably, require assurance that you are motivated; that you have the competence to perform the role; that you have the knowledge to pass course assessments; and that you are committed to their service.

Managers are more likely to offer you a development opportunity if they are presented with current examples of your work that demonstrate your competence, motivation and work ethic, all of which can be detailed in future applications and personal statements. Inevitably, application and interview processes will be competitive for highly sought-after roles/ courses; therefore, you need to meticulously prepare for interviews, align current examples from practice and give people a reason to choose you!

Note: Offering to support local projects that are aligned to a defined career pathway will inevitably aid your future progression. However, this does not mean you should work vastly beyond the boundaries of your current banding, or be taken advantage of by a senior who delegates too much. There needs to be clear communication between you and your line manager to ensure you both benefit from any additional tasks you choose to take on, which should be clearly defined within your professional development plans (see *Section 2.4* on PDRs).

### 3.1.2 How do I stop procrastinating?

Realistically, we all have times when we procrastinate amid life's busy schedules at work and home. It is natural to procrastinate, i.e. avoid or put off doing something you find challenging, when faced with difficult clinical situations or barriers to change in your practice. However, procrastination can cause you additional anxiety if challenges are avoided for long periods and may halt your career progression if it prevents you starting or completing project work.

Communicating with a challenging colleague who has upset you, documenting several care plan evaluations at the end of a chaotic 12-hour shift, completing a looming dissertation or clinical report on time, completing three-yearly NMC revalidation documents, working in teams with high staff sickness rates, performance managing a member of staff, creating three months of team rotas in advance: all of these examples may cause individuals to feel additional pressure. When you feel stressed your survival instinct kicks in; you may focus on your immediate needs as opposed to others, and your subconscious says: "Really, do we have to? Let's go to the pub instead, or watch TV, or scroll through Twitter, or avoid entering the room if a certain person is in there, or do my assignment/ project work next week, or the week after that…"

Throughout your career you should aim to develop ways to avoid procrastination and manage your time effectively wherever possible. Identifying strategies to avoid procrastination will help you make positive decisions and implement changes that will support your future development.

**KEY TIP**

- Breaking a large task into smaller achievable goals will help you to get started and avoid procrastination.

See *Table 3.1* for more tips to avoid procrastination.

### 3.1.3 Identify strategies to prevent and manage stress before taking on new projects

Before you contemplate contributing to, or initiating, any new project that may add to your current workload, it is very important that you find a work–life balance and learn to manage your time effectively first. Otherwise you may be at risk of becoming overwhelmed and feeling overloaded at work, which may eventually lead to stress-related illness. All staff need to learn how to identify when they are becoming stressed and have strategies in place to prevent stress and manage their stress levels during the course of their whole career (see *Section 6.2.4* for further guidance on managing and preventing stress in the workplace).

*Table 3.1:* Tips to avoid procrastination

| Key tip | Further guidance |
|---|---|
| Keep things in perspective | • Try to keep things in perspective and don't dwell on the negative, such as how big the challenge ahead is<br>• Everyone procrastinates at times so don't be hard on yourself, and try to put unhelpful past behaviours behind you |
| Break down a large job into smaller goals | • The most important method to avoid procrastination is to break a big job down into smaller, achievable, short-term goals<br>• Use smaller sub-headings if you have a large narrative assignment to complete; splitting an assignment/report/dissertation into sections and bite-sized chunks will make it much more achievable<br>• You can use as many small goals/sub-headings as you need and allocate time slots to them, e.g. I will complete my 200-word introduction in this 3-hour period/by end of today; or 3 weeks of staffing rotas will be completed over 3 days, or 24 hrs worth of rota will be completed each successive day<br>• Don't set unrealistic goals, e.g. if you know you have a family wedding to go to, then timetable a break that weekend rather than completing your dissertation methodology! Or, if you know your manager is on annual leave try to complete important jobs or book admin time before or after, as you may be busier if deputising while they are away |
| Schedule calendar time and set regular deadlines | • When blocking out time, schedule tasks in your calendar<br>• Set yourself deadlines using realistic time frames when allocating slots (if in doubt always overestimate; you are avoiding the task for a reason and it may take you longer than you anticipate!)<br>• Ask your manager or relevant others to help guide your timings if you are unsure or you find it difficult to manage your time effectively |
| Start with what you like 'best' or get the 'worst' over first | • Think about completing the easiest or worst task first, depending on the situation and your preference<br>• If you need to have a difficult conversation with a colleague to complete a report, it may be easier to take a deep breath and just start this conversation first to get the hardest task over with; alternatively, you may enjoy doing research, reviewing articles or talking to people for inspiration before you start to write up an important report or business plan<br>• Once you have taken the first step, however small, it is more likely to motivate you to keep going |

*Table 3.1:* *(continued)*

| Key tip | Further guidance |
|---------|------------------|
| Set a timer | • If you have a real block on starting a difficult project, set a timer and work solely on one task for a set period<br>• Just 15 minutes can be enough to motivate you (obviously if you can do an hour or more, go for it!)<br>• Having the timer and a set time slot in your diary, although it sounds prescriptive, can help some people break the habit of 'avoidance' (I find this technique really useful to get over a psychological barrier to begin a particularly tedious report) |
| Remove all distractions | • Make your environment conducive to completing the task, e.g. work in a quiet room/library or away from your children or chatty colleagues in an open office<br>• Turn off any distractions such as social media, your phone/TV<br>• Ask your manager to work from home or away from your workplace to complete a set project |
| Plan and prepare first | • If you really can't face the task in hand, at least spend time preparing as much as you can first to make it easier to start a project<br>• You can collect resources, folders and information to assist you or tidy and organise your surroundings prior to beginning a project |
| Be realistic about what you can achieve | • Although you should aim to complete tasks to the best of your ability, sometimes perfectionism will stop you finishing a project; sometimes 'good enough' is all you can manage at the time and 'good enough' is sufficient<br>• Use a team approach and ask others to help you choose an alternative easier option if you are unsure about what is realistic and feasible |
| Ask for help and/or delegate | • Break a large project down into individual tasks that can be delegated to other team members according to their skill set<br>• If you are really struggling, never hesitate to ask for additional support; a trusted friend or colleague can give you an alternative perspective – they may have completed a similar project or can link you to others who can offer constructive advice |
| Reward yourself when you complete goals | • Give yourself a reward when you complete a difficult challenge, as it will help to motivate you, e.g. book a holiday or theatre trip, or treat yourself to something special |

## 3.2 WE ALL HAVE THE POWER TO POSITIVELY INFLUENCE CHANGE IN OUR CURRENT ROLE

While working in pressurised healthcare environments it is normal for staff to sometimes offload to colleagues when faced with difficult challenges. Talking about your anxieties enables you to seek support from others and de-stress. However, constant negativity and complaining can be demotivating and eventually demoralise a whole team. Alternatively, influencing positive change and supporting initiatives within your current role will help benefit services and your future career development.

I hope that the practice examples in this chapter may help inspire you in the future to influence, inform, and contribute to patient care and your profession.

### 3.2.1  Anyone can influence positive change in practice, including you!

All staff have the potential to implement a new initiative or promote a positive change in practice if the project is supported by the right people, the proposal is underpinned by a relevant evidence base, there is a structured evaluation to measure impact and staff are motivated to implement the change. You may not want to initiate or lead a project; but there are several ways you can collaborate and make a valuable contribution.

**One simple idea**

A simple idea from one person who is passionate about changing the status quo, can snowball into a national campaign and lead to changes being implemented. The #hellomynameis campaign is a clear example of how one person can have a massive impact on the delivery of future healthcare globally, using social media.

In 2013, Dr Kate Granger was diagnosed as terminally ill and underwent cancer treatment as an inpatient in hospital. She observed that many staff did not introduce themselves before delivering care. She felt passionate about the need for better communication and set about using social media to remind healthcare staff about the importance of introductions in healthcare. Kate Granger created the simple introduction 'hello my name is....' for healthcare staff to use when introducing themselves to all patients. As momentum gathered, the media campaign took off and since #hellomynameis was conceived, there have been over 2 billion online engagements with this initiative across the world. This incredibly successful campaign has grown into a global phenomenon that is influencing healthcare interactions across the world today. It is amazing to know that Kate's legacy lives on after her death.

## National campaigns

Successful national campaigns may be led by individuals or professional bodies/institutions who request change for the benefit of others. The 2019 RCN 'Safe staffing' campaign led by RCN President Anne Marie Rafferty, CBE, is a prime example of this, as the RCN calls for "safe and effective care to be enshrined in law in each UK country" through the introduction of "safe staffing laws for nursing" (RCN, 2019a). The RCN has encouraged 435 000 RCN members to become involved in this campaign by responding to a consultation online, which requests legal changes to the Health and Social Care Act (2012) aiming to improve staff shortages and meet patients' needs (RCN, 2019b).

Rather than just reactively complaining about staffing levels that are imposed on staff, we can all contribute to local and national projects by answering online surveys and commenting on consultation papers, to influence positive change within your profession. I, for one, have signed online to support the RCN 'Safe staffing' campaign and hope to see legally mandated safe staffing nursing levels and ratios in each UK country in my lifetime.

## Become a 'contributor' and join a working party or service improvement group

Any staff member may become part of a working group to implement a service improvement project, or to inform and evaluate future professional and government policies, standards, recommendations and regulations. In fact, most employers actively request a range of staff members to volunteer across different bands to support local clinical governance and service improvement projects, especially during the implementation and evaluation stage (see *Table 3.4*).

## Service improvement projects and evaluations

Positive change may come to fruition through effective team work and local service evaluations. Bradley and Rees (2003) provide a clear example of how a local service evaluation carried out by a working party influenced patient care. Local changes were implemented to support vulnerable patients who needed nutritional assistance. Red food trays were used to indicate patients who were unable to feed themselves on a trauma rehabilitation unit. Senior staff nurse Lindsey Bradley initially came up with the simple 'red tray' idea and it was evident, following an audit evaluation, that at-risk patients could be identified and better supported with their meals using colour-coded trays (Bradley and Rees, 2003).

Other clinical areas across the NHS were inspired by Bradley and Rees to implement similar approaches, such as Hollis (2011) who describes how a local working party audited the use of red colour-coded jugs and mugs on a trauma orthopaedic ward for patients at risk of dehydration. Both Bradley and Rees's (2003) and Hollis's (2011) audits highlight the need for effective team work to help implement service improvements. They also demonstrate the importance of evaluating the change implemented prior to rolling it out across the service, which helps sustain a service improvement in the long term (see *change management models* and *audits* in *Table 3.4*).

## Disseminate data through publications

Hollis's (2011) acknowledgement of how Bradley and Rees's (2003) audit evaluation influenced her project highlights the impact of disseminating findings in a national publication to inspire and influence others. Publishing can range from a small piece in a local newsletter or a systematic review that highlights existing knowledge and current gaps in a specialist field, to a 5000-word article presenting a multi-method research project in a national journal. Writing up a service evaluation, or a change you have implemented in practice, or describing your experiences, may support others who are dealing with similar practice issues (see *Section 7.3* on how to publish your work).

## Connect with others and embrace social media

If you have a specialist interest then aim to connect with like-minded people locally and nationally. You may wish to join an already established working group or set up a new partnership to generate ideas if there is nothing currently in place. Many patient charities and professional bodies welcome enthusiastic and motivated new members to share and disseminate data.

Nowadays, staff can network widely and easily using social media to communicate initiatives and share ideas. There are many professional networks and online forums that you can join to keep up to date with the latest initiatives. Numerous newly qualified professionals are running on-line blogs and creating videos to share their experiences, and professional bodies are disseminating updates through their Facebook and Twitter sites.

KEY TIP

- If you are engaging on social media sites you should review the NMC's (2015) *Guidance on Using Social Media Responsibly*; for example, you should never post pictures of "patients and people receiving care without their consent" or "discuss matters related to the people in [your] care outside clinical settings".

## Professional knowledge and research

Never underestimate the power of professional knowledge and research as a basis to influence change. Florence Nightingale was the first nurse researcher to share her knowledge widely and publish her research findings. She used survey instruments, graphical data and pie charts to disseminate her findings, such as high mortality rates relating to "certain conditions" (Nightingale, 1859). Florence Nightingale was also the first nurse researcher to compare mortality rates associated with care delivered by trained vs. untrained nurses. These findings enabled her to secure financial support to establish the first training school for nurses at St Thomas' Hospital, London (Nightingale, 1863). Essentially, Florence Nightingale was able to use her nursing knowledge and research findings as powerful tools to assure the future professionalisation of nursing; hence she is referred to today as the founder of nursing globally.

Professional knowledge and research remain synonymous with power as they continue to influence changes in healthcare practice. During professional graduate training programmes, healthcare students are taught to critically appraise an evidence base to answer a specific research question, which enables them to apply the best available evidence to the decisions they make in clinical practice, essentially providing 'evidence-based practice' (see *Table 3.3*).

The development of critical research skills enables you to become 'research-active', to question what is going on around you, to identify gaps in current knowledge, to support the implementation of new research or service improvement projects and to reinforce your opinions as a catalyst for change. Healthcare students studying for a level 6 degree will complete a dissertation research project and throughout your career you should aim to remain research-active to influence change in the future (see further guidance to support research activity in *Section 7.2*).

## Share your knowledge with others

All staff can share their knowledge and expertise with others, and act as good role models in practice. Even if you are new to a role, you may have a passion that can be shared to benefit others.

Any staff member can share their knowledge by offering to do the following:

### Support recruitment events

- Attend local recruitment events and/or visit schools to inspire others to choose a similar career pathway. I often ask apprentices and junior staff to attend our recruitment events, as potential applicants find it helpful to talk to new starters about their experiences. Having an experienced staff member who is approachable and passionate about their specialist area will inspire attendees to apply for posts.
- If you cannot attend a recruitment event, then create some resources instead – e.g. a short piece of narrative detailing the support you have received – or devise flyers and marketing materials.

### Orientate staff

- You can orientate new starters across all bands. Senior staff require orientating to their new surroundings and responsibilities, just as much as junior staff (see *Table 2.1*).
- Offer to conduct walk-round inductions, support the completion of role-specific competencies and professional development plans, or create a resource folder to help familiarise others with their new role. You may have a better understanding of what helps a new starter if you have recently experienced an orientation yourself.

### Develop documentation

- Assist in the writing of local documentation such as competencies, standards, policies, guidelines or care plans (see the key terms in *Section 3.4*).

### Teach and support others

- Contribute to supervising, assessing or coaching others.
- Teach others, e.g. present a PowerPoint or teaching poster explaining anatomy and physiology to colleagues; facilitate a discussion relating to a specialist area of interest; act as a link person to disseminate evidence-based practice, or develop a resource folder to update staff with the latest professional guidelines (see *Section 5.2.1*).
- Assist in local health education activities such as designing patient educational posters to be placed in reception areas.

### Help lead local project work

Ask local managers and specialist leads how you can support local projects. See examples below relating to different bands:

### Band 5
- Join a corporate-led documentation group to review and update evidence-based care plans.
- Act as a link nurse for a specific condition or specialist area.
- Evaluate different types of clinical practice, such as clinical handovers or visiting times.

### Band 6
- Complete staffing rotas for an allocated period of time.
- Lead or facilitate a staff/patient support group.
- Collaborate with a charity to support individuals with specialist needs.

### Band 7
- Lead a clinical governance group on behalf of a matron.
- Lead a FallSafe project and its implementation across several services.
- Visit other professionals in the UK delivering unique clinic services to inform a new autonomously-led clinic or set up a new health promotion programme.

 **KEY TIP**

- All staff members, whatever level they are, have the power to positively influence change and support initiatives that benefit patients, staff, services or their profession.

## 3.3 UNDERSTAND THE LOCAL AND NATIONAL SYSTEMS IN WHICH YOU WORK

As a healthcare professional, you work within organisational structures and frameworks defined by government, legal and professional bodies. It helps to have an understanding of procedures and guidelines from key national institutions/associations to progress future projects.

When supporting or implementing a change in practice, you need to work with others to successfully plan, implement, evaluate and sustain/revise changes long term. Whilst championing projects or new initiatives you may overcome resistance from staff, systems or organisations by:

- working within a supportive organisational culture
- engaging with supportive leads and managers
- utilising an evidence base that supports change
- engaging with national advisory bodies and professional institutions
- establishing realistic project timelines and avoiding complicated processes
- working with competent and willing staff.

(McSherry and Pearce, 2007; Gottwald and Lansdown, 2014; de Silva, 2015).

### 3.3.1 *The need for consent and authorisation*

If you wish to develop a new initiative within your work environment, such as becoming a link nurse/midwife or starting a support group, you should always discuss plans with your line manager and seek their consent and authorisation.

Your line manager and education lead can offer helpful advice, such as meeting the local NHS Trust tissue viability lead if you plan to become a link person for tissue viability. You may need to attend a 'train the trainer' course to increase your knowledge of current procedures and be signed off as competent to act as a 'resource link or lead'. Link nurses/midwives can also network nationally, attend conference days and collaborate with specialist charities.

Delivering a PowerPoint, facilitating staff support sessions or workshops, leading a working party or clinical governance group will require local consent and authorisation from your manager and shift coordinator for sessions to take place on the day. You will need authorisation to establish the following:

- Am I the right person to be leading the session/group meeting and am I qualified to do the role?
- Is this project suitable for the local area and/or is it overlapping a current group/session elsewhere?
- Should there be a team to assist with delivery and share the workload with me?
- Who is the best person to guide this initiative if I need additional advice, e.g. on how often sessions should take place?
- How long is it feasible for staff to leave the clinical/community work setting to attend my session/group meetings?

- What content should be delivered to help staff learning?
- What national guidelines/procedures should be incorporated, adhered to, or referenced as part of my sessions/meetings? It is important that you adhere to national risk assessments and health and safety laws.
- Are there specific times that should be avoided when delivering sessions, to ensure patients and safe staffing levels are not put at risk?
- Who is the key person to authorise any group plans or future actions/recommendations?

Similarly, a recruitment event, conference or charitable event, which involves staff leaving a clinical area, should be authorised by the relevant managers who need to maintain an overview of staffing numbers. Always find out who should authorise an event at the planning stage to prevent concerns being raised later. An email to gain written authorisation for a local event should be obtained from the relevant managers.

 **KEY TIP**

- If you are responsible for organising event stands outside normal lecture/seminar rooms, such as in corridors or high traffic reception areas, you usually require formal authorisation from an estate department lead and a department manager. Estate departments will request that a risk assessment is carried out, and that you, as the event's organiser, sign a risk assessment form to assure public safety, which you must confirm prior to planning an event.

### 3.3.2 *Formal ethical approval and consent*

Always establish who the correct person is to authorise local research and service improvement projects. You will need to obtain formal consent from local managers and research leads prior to conducting any research study in a clinical area or community setting. Helpful information regarding formal applications to ethics committees is found on the National Institute for Health Research (NIHR) website (see NIHR responsibilities, *Table 3.2*). You will also find national research funding opportunities, study grants and scholarships on the NIHR website to support research initiatives (see *Section 7.2.6*).

Health service research studies must follow national procedures devised by the UK Health Research Authority (HRA) (Marshall, 2006;

Pick *et al.*, 2013) and uphold the principles of the Mental Health Act (2007). Helpful online guidance and toolkits are available from the HRA and Medical Research Council (MRC, 2019) that provide:

- information on the principles of consent
- guides for designing consent and participant information forms
- additional practical case examples and templates.

A clinical audit as part of a service improvement evaluation does not usually require submission to a research ethics committee (REC). Audits and service evaluations should, however, assure sensitivity to the needs and rights of individuals, and still be conducted within an ethical framework that adheres to the Data Protection Act (2018) and the Caldicott Principles (Caldicott Committee, 1997) to safeguard information and maintain confidentiality.

 **KEY TIP**

- Some service improvement projects require formal ethical approval due to the data collection and methods used. It is important to take advice from local and national research leads if you are unsure whether your service improvement project requires formal ethical approval.

### 3.3.3 Authorisation for procedures, policies and guidelines

Prior to reviewing or developing clinical policies and guidelines, you must inform your line manager and any appointed working groups for policy development, such as your local Quality and Safety Committee. It is your responsibility to establish what procedure is involved, as policies always require formal authorisation prior to being disseminated for wider use across organisations and community settings. New policies and guidelines will be rigorously scrutinised and either returned for amendments or approved to go forward for formal authorisation. Once ratified, policies may be published on the internet and need to hold up to public scrutiny, which is why they go through rigorous review processes before approval.

Typically working groups for policy development and Quality Safety Committees will be led by an associate director lead, responsible for ensuring that policies meet exacting standards. Employers should have a local policy specifically for the development and management of procedural documents, which you must adhere to. All policies must be referenced and informed by relevant national standards and frameworks.

It is helpful to download a diagram from your employer's intranet site that details key departments, senior personnel and specialist leads placed in hierarchical order of responsibility. Alternatively, your HR department or line manager should have electronic copies to advise who to contact for authorisation.

### 3.3.4  Adhere to media and communication standards

If you are organising or supporting a conference day or recruitment fair, then you must obtain a 'sign-off' authorisation for the marketing and educational materials used at the event. Your local media and communications team will ensure that narrative on brochures, flyers and the internet, or broadcasts on local radio, meet corporate communication standards. However, a media and communications team will not check any field-related content. This must be signed off by a department manager for accuracy before being sent to the media and communications department.

Media and communications teams will check that there are no grammatical or technical errors in the information being disseminated, such as spelling mistakes, the wrong corporate logo or inaccurate job titles. It is especially important that there is a final sign-off on marketing brochures and flyers before you pay external companies for costly printing or complete hundreds of photocopies.

Media teams are responsible for managing all internal and external communications and will use a wide-reaching approach to promote events on local and national online social platforms, which helps to increase the number of attendees. Try to use your media and communications teams' expertise as much as possible to make your event a great success.

### 3.3.5  Standards for patient information

If you wish to create new patient information leaflets they will be subject to a defined local review process, such as: a local lead to advise; a sign-off person to authorise content; an ongoing content review every three years to assure national updates are amended; and a consultation with local equity and diversity leads. Never design, produce or distribute patient information leaflets without reviewing local and national policy, procedure and guidelines first.

Similarly, health education activities providing individuals with information need to adhere to processes that assure the accuracy of content. Any health education posters, brochures, flyers or online material being placed in public areas should align to organisational standards and be underpinned by the current evidence base.

The Medicines and Healthcare products Regulatory Agency (2015) *Best Practice Guidance on Patient Information Leaflets* sets out the legal framework for patient information leaflets and best practice relating to information, language and design, as described in EU and national legislation; for example, the NHS logo must be top right.

### 3.3.6 *What is out there already to inform your work?*

Systematic reviews are widely considered the most valid form of medical evidence and level 6 graduate healthcare professionals are taught how to formulate a research question and conduct a systematic review to inform the delivery of healthcare (Higgins and Green, 2008; Khan *et al.*, 2003). Through systematically reviewing an evidence base you can critically analyse previous studies to inform a future project, identify any gaps in the current evidence base and ensure future work adheres to national regulations, frameworks and guidelines (see *Table 3.3*).

Electronic digitised databases are provided in all healthcare libraries, and librarians regularly offer staff demonstrations to access online systems at work or from home effectively. Librarians will guide staff who need additional support using Boolean operators, that help to combine key search words, synonyms and truncations, and to widen or narrow searches within the MEDLINE, CINAHL, EMBASE, PsycINFO, BNI, AMED and Cochrane Library databases.

### 3.3.7 *Share ideas, resources and experiences with others*

Prior to planning any new initiative, it is helpful to network with colleagues and specialist leads to share ideas, resources and experiences, as it prevents the risk of repetition and 'reinventing the wheel'. You may find that there is already an established group and no more projects are needed, or that you can pursue a different angle in an alternative area.

Collaborating with individuals who have completed similar work can save you hours of time, as you may be able to adapt an already established service improvement, presentation, audit tool, staff induction, care plan or documentation standard. Any work adapted from others should always be clearly acknowledged in your title, e.g. 'Career pathways adapted from Forde-Johnston (2018)' and include full reference. You must adhere to UK copyright laws and never plagiarise narrative from publications. It is also polite to inform staff that you wish to adapt their unpublished work and assure them that you will acknowledge their contribution.

If there are no individuals or local working groups to guide you, then consider networking with national leads through professional and government bodies. National organisational structures are summarised below, followed by an overview of professional and legal governing institutions/bodies.

### 3.3.8 Understand national organisational structures

#### NHS Trusts

NHS Trusts are public sector businesses headed by a board of directors and executive/non-executive members at the top of the organisation (their photos are usually found on Trust websites). The Trust board of directors has overall responsibility for the Trust strategy, which includes making sure that activity meets demand and that the Trust meets quality targets set by the government, whilst keeping within fixed financial budgets. Within NHS Trusts there is always a democratically elected council of governors – unpaid members that hold the Trust board to account. All Trust boards are required to have an audit committee consisting only of non-executive directors.

The Trust management executive is the senior managerial decision-making body and is usually chaired by the chief executive. The chief executive will be the person called to give interviews to the media if there are any local issues, or new initiatives to promote. Key executive staff will hold information-sharing meetings open to all employees to keep them updated on future strategic plans. These open forums are usually advertised on local intranet pages or work email and are interesting to attend, as they give staff an opportunity to put forward their perspectives on the services being delivered.

Trust services will be split into clinical services that are usually led by a divisional director or general manager. If you work for a Trust it is helpful to find out how departments are structured and where your department sits relative to other services. There will always be a head nurse and/or chief operating officer responsible for all nursing and midwifery staff, sometimes called a lead nurse, director of nursing and midwifery, chief nurse or clinical nurse and midwifery director. It is helpful to know who the senior nurses and midwives are under the lead, such as your divisional nurse/midwife, matron or assistant/deputy matron.

## Structures in community care settings

In 2013, the structures in community care settings were changed, following the creation of Clinical Commissioning Groups (CCGs) which replaced primary care Trusts (PCTs). CCGs are clinically-led statutory bodies responsible for the planning and commissioning of health services for a local area. CCGs are structured as membership bodies, with local general practitioner (GP) practices as members. They are controlled by an elected governing body made up of GPs and other clinicians, which should include a lay member, a registered nurse and a secondary care consultant. CCGs are responsible for commissioning mental health services, emergency care, rehabilitation care, elective hospital services and community care, and are answerable to the Secretary of State for Health through NHS England.

## Private sector employers

Private sector employers, such as a private nursing home, are not bound by standard NHS structures as they are classed as privately owned businesses. A typical private nursing home will be headed by a director of operations who is responsible for making sure that the overall business goals are met. In a large nursing home there may be a number of assistant directors. The director of operations is usually the face of the nursing home and in charge of administration. They have a key role in obtaining external funding from sponsors and marketing their service, and they are not involved in the day-to-day care of patients.

The majority of nursing homes employ a chief nursing officer (they may have a different title) who is responsible for managing all employees who deliver direct care and ensuring that nursing standards are maintained. In contrast to a chief nursing officer, nurse managers in nursing homes are responsible for a smaller number of staff and residents, and they report to the chief nursing officer.

## Private hospitals

Private hospitals often have a similar structure to nursing homes in relation to operational management; however, ratios of trained to untrained nurses are different, as nursing homes usually use a higher ratio of nursing assistants to registered nurses. Private hospitals often have the same senior nursing structures as NHS hospitals.

### *3.3.9 Key national institutions and professional bodies*

#### Department of Health (DH)

Role
Ministerial department responsible for government policy on health and social care.

Key responsibilities
- Overseeing the National Health Service (NHS)
- Providing strategic leadership and funding for the NHS, public health and social care
- Developing and creating national policies and guidelines to improve the quality of care, meet health care demands and patients' expectations
- Providing long-term vision to address future health care challenges
- Assuring the delivery of services and their continuity
- Representing the best interests of the public, patient and taxpayer.

#### Secretary of State for Health

Role
Government cabinet minister with responsibility for the work of the Department of Health (DH).

Key responsibilities
- Responsibility for health in the NHS, which includes the policies of the department, financial control, performance and delivery, and patient safety.

#### NHS England/Scotland/Wales; Health and Social Care Northern Ireland

Role
Executive non-departmental public bodies of the Department of Health.

Key responsibilities
- Setting priorities and direction in the NHS to improve healthcare outcomes for people
- Focusing on the operational side and delivery of commissioning in the NHS.

## Public Health England (PHE); NHS Health Scotland; Public Health Wales; Public Health Agency in Northern Ireland

Role
Executive agencies of the Department of Health.

Key responsibilities
- Providing national leadership and expert services to support public health
- Working with local government and the NHS to respond to emergencies
- Providing education for the public to make healthier choices
- Addressing health care inequalities.

## Care Quality Commission (CQC)

Role
Executive non-departmental public body of the Department of Health.

Key responsibilities
- Independently regulating and inspecting health and social care services in England
- Ensuring that healthcare services in England provide people with safe and effective care
- Encouraging care services to improve through carrying out inspections and monitoring data that can indicate problems
- Registering care providers and rating services
- Taking action to protect patients who use services and to protect the rights of vulnerable people.

## NHS Improvement (NHSI)

Role
Regulatory body bringing together several non-departmental public bodies of the NHS.

Key responsibilities
- Ensuring foundation Trusts, NHS Trusts and independent providers are financially and clinically sustainable through embedding systems for quality improvement.

## Nursing and Midwifery Council (NMC)

Role
Statutory regulating professional body for nursing and midwifery professionals in the UK.

Key responsibilities
• Maintaining a national register of all nurses, midwives and specialist community public health nurses and nursing associates eligible to practise within the UK
• Protecting the public by setting standards of nurse education, training, conduct and performance
• Investigating allegations of incompetence and impaired fitness to practise.

## National Institute for Health and Care Excellence (NICE)

Role
Executive non-departmental public body of the Department of Health in the UK.

Key responsibilities
• Providing a national evidence base to guide improvements to health for the public and patients (originally set up to end the 'postcode lottery')
• Providing information and developing quality standards for those commissioning health, public health and social care services
• Appraising the use of health technologies, treatments and procedures within the NHS to guide practice on appropriate treatment.

## Royal College of Nursing; Royal College of Midwives

Role
Professional membership organisation and trade union for nurses and midwives in the UK.

Key responsibilities
• Promoting excellence in practice and shaping UK health policies
• Representing the professional interests of nursing/midwifery staff working in the public, private and voluntary sectors
• Lobbying UK institutions and bodies to develop, influence and implement policies to improve quality care

- Providing expert advice to parliamentarians on developing healthcare policies through legislation, select committees, all-party parliamentary groups and parliamentary briefings
- Attending major UK party conferences, whilst maintaining political independence
- Supporting and approving nursing/midwifery standards, education and practice
- Hosting a specialist library in London (the largest in Europe)
- Providing grants through the RCN Foundation for nursing and midwifery-led research and projects, as well as education and hardship support
- Collaborating with key UK bodies to negotiate pay, and terms and conditions, for public and independent sector nurses.

## Health Education England (HEE); NHS Education for Scotland (NES); Health Education and Improvement Wales (HEIW); Department of Health, Social Services and Public Safety (DHSSPS) Northern Ireland (NI)

Role
Executive non-departmental public bodies of the Department of Health.

Key responsibilities
- Responsibility for national leadership, coordination and commissioning of education and training within the health/public health workforce
- Providing national consistency and standards to fund and support the training of a range of multi-professional staff and apprentices
- Collaborating with several key departments to deliver education and training such as:
  - the DH, NHSI, CQC and PHE to deliver the *NHS Long Term Plan* in England (NHS England, 2019a)
  - the Northern Ireland Practice and Education Council for Nursing and Midwifery (NIPEC) and Northern Ireland Medical and Dental Training Agency (NIMDTA)
  - the Workforce, Education and Development Services (WEDS), now part of HEIW
  - the Joint Improvement Team (JIT), NHS Scotland, COSLA (Convention of Scottish Local Authorities) and the Scottish Social Services Council (SSSC).

### National Institute for Health Research (NIHR)

Role
Government-funded institute to support clinical research.

Key responsibilities
- Funding high quality research to improve health through bursaries, grants and training programmes that support health researchers
- Providing world-class research facilities and support services, such as the research design service (www.nihr.ac.uk/explore-nihr/support/research-design-service.htm)
- Working with life sciences industries and charities to benefit patients and the public.

### NHS Centre for Reviews and Dissemination (NHS CARD)

Role
NHS health services research centre.
- Providing the NHS with important information on the effectiveness and cost-effectiveness of treatments, and the delivery and organisation of healthcare
- Offering rigorous and systematic reviews of research on selected topics, a database of quality-assessed published reviews, and a dissemination service
- Providing evidence to improve outcomes for patients and inform decisions on the effectiveness, efficiency and safety of healthcare systems
- Collaborating with international communities on applied global health research for the benefit of patients and the public.

## 3.4 OVERVIEW OF KEY TERMS

It is helpful to be aware of key terminology in relation to supporting others and influencing change, e.g. in order to guide project work that you wish to lead or support.

 **KEY TIP**

- You will find this terminology useful for interview preparation as well.

The following tables present an overview of key terms you may come across under these four headings:

1. Teaching, supervising and supporting others (*Table 3.2*)
2. Evidence-based practice and research (*Table 3.3*)
3. Improving quality of care (*Table 3.4*)
4. Management and leadership (*Table 3.5*).

The key terms are not meant to be exhaustive, and indicative references provide further guidance.

*Table 3.2: Teaching, supervising and supporting others*

| Terms and key references | Further guidance |
|---|---|
| Mentor (NMC, 2008) | • The term 'mentor' has been phased out by the NMC and replaced with three new supervisory and assessor roles: practice supervisor, practice assessor and academic assessor (*see below*) (NMC, 2018a)<br>• 'Mentor' referred to a registered nurse or midwife who acted as a facilitator of learning, supervisor and assessor for students in practice (NMC, 2008)<br>• Each student had a named mentor to give feedback on their development and progress during a defined placement period |
| Practice supervisor (NMC, 2018a) | • Contributes to the student's record of achievement by periodically recording relevant observations on their conduct, proficiency and achievement of the students they are supervising<br>• Contributes to student assessments to inform decisions for progression<br>• Engages with practice assessors and academic assessors to share relevant observations on the conduct, proficiency and achievement of the students they are supervising<br>• Appropriately raises and responds to student conduct and competence concerns<br>• Receives ongoing support to prepare, reflect and develop effective supervisions and contributes to student learning and assessment<br>• Understands the proficiencies and programme outcomes they are supporting students to achieve.<br>• Serves as a role model for safe and effective practice in line with the NMC (2018b) Code of conduct<br>• Supports and supervises students, providing feedback on their progress<br>• Has current knowledge and experience in the area in which they are providing support and supervision<br>• Receives ongoing support to participate in the practice learning of students |
| Practice assessor NMC (2018a) | • Conducts assessments to confirm study achievement of proficiencies and programme outcomes for practice learning<br>• Assessment decisions by practice assessors are informed by feedback received from practice supervisors<br>• Makes and records objective, evidence-based assessments on conduct, proficiency and achievement, drawing on student records, direct observation and student self-reflection |

*Table 3.2: (continued)*

| Terms and key references | Further guidance |
|---|---|
| | • Maintains current knowledge and expertise relevant for the proficiencies and programme outcomes they are assessing<br>• Works in partnership with a nominated academic assessor to evaluate and recommend the student for progression for each part of their programme<br>• Has an understanding of the student's learning and achievement in theory<br>• Communicates and collaborates between practice and academic assessors at scheduled relevant points during student progression<br>• Practice assessors are not simultaneously the practice supervisor and academic assessor for the same student<br>• Undertakes preparation, or provides evidence of prior learning experience, which enables them to demonstrate:<br>  – interpersonal skills relevant to student learning and assessment<br>  – objective, evidence-based assessments of students<br>  – constructive feedback to facilitate professional development in others<br>  – knowledge of the assessment process and their role within it<br>• Receives ongoing support and training to develop their role<br>• Proactively develops their professional practice and knowledge to fulfil their role<br>• Understands the proficiencies and programme outcomes that the students are aiming to achieve |
| Academic assessor (NMC, 2018a) | • Collates and confirms student achievement of proficiencies and programme outcomes in the academic environment for each part of the programme<br>• Records objective, evidence-based decisions on conduct, proficiency and achievement<br>• Provides recommendations for progression, drawing on student records and other resources<br>• Maintains current knowledge and expertise relevant for the proficiencies and programme outcomes they are assessing and confirming<br>• Works in partnership with a nominated practice assessor to evaluate and recommend the student for progression for each part of their programme<br>• Has an understanding of the student's learning and achievement in practice<br>• Communicates and collaborates between academic and practice assessors at scheduled relevant points during student progression<br>• Academic assessors are not simultaneously the practice supervisor and practice assessor for the same student |
| Reflection (Gibbs, 1988; Johns, 2000; Bulman and Schutz, 2013) | • Process of making sense of an experience in order to move on and do better as a practitioner (Bulman *et al.*, 2012)<br>• Schön (1991) presented the concept of 'reflection in action' and 'reflection on action', i.e. there are two types of reflection, one during an activity or event, and one after (see *Section 6.2.2*)<br>• Frameworks for reflection have been offered by theorists such as Gibbs (1988) and Johns (2000) |

*Table 3.2: (continued)*

| Terms and key references | Further guidance |
|---|---|
| | • Gibbs (1988) developed the widely used Reflective Cycle, which includes six stages:<br>– description of the experience<br>– feelings and thoughts about the experience<br>– evaluation of the experience<br>– analysis to make sense of the situation<br>– conclusion about what you learned and what you could have done differently<br>– action plan for how you would deal with similar situations in the future<br>• Oelofsen (2012) developed a framework called the 3-step (CLT) Reflective Cycle to structure reflections as follows:<br>– Step 1: Curiosity – involves noticing things, asking questions and questioning assumptions<br>– Step 2: Looking closer – involves looking at a situation in detail, finding words that help to make sense of what has happened, being open to alternative perspectives and ideas, thinking about the situation from other positions and not falling back on accepted assumptions or methods<br>– Step 3: Transformation and feedback – involves bringing together the thoughts and ideas from the first two steps to find ways of thinking about how a situation might be different and how positive changes can be made |
| Clinical supervision (CQC, 2013; Pollock *et al.*, 2017) | • Formal process of learning and professional support using a non-judgemental approach to support an individual's developmental needs<br>• Involves a supportive relationship between a supervisor and a supervisee using a working agreement that facilitates reflective learning<br>• Provides a safe and confidential environment for you to reflect on practice and discuss issues from work<br>• Reflects different models and there are several types that can be adapted to suit local environments (CQC, 2013; Pollock *et al.*, 2017):<br>– managerial supervision:<br>  ◦ carried out by a supervisor with authority who has accountability for the supervisee<br>  ◦ provides the opportunity for staff to review their performance, set objectives in line with service priorities and identify their development needs<br>– clinical supervision:<br>  ◦ provides the opportunity for staff to reflect on and review their practice<br>  ◦ provides the opportunity to discuss individual cases in depth, change/modify their practice, and identify individuals' development needs<br>– professional supervision (often used interchangeably with clinical supervision):<br>  ◦ supervision carried out by another member of the same professional group (they may work in a completely different department or for another employer)<br>  ◦ provides staff with the opportunity to review professional standards, identify training and development needs and ensure they are working to national standards |

*Table 3.2: (continued)*

| Terms and key references | Further guidance |
|---|---|
| | • All registered nurses and midwives should have access to clinical supervision for the duration of their career to develop their knowledge, skills and competence in practice<br>• A clinical supervisor is allocated to clinically supervise you individually (a 1:1 clinical supervision approach) or within a clinical supervision group<br>• Some employers allocate a clinical supervisor when you start in practice; others wait for you to request a supervisor |
| Action learning (McGill and Beaty, 1992; Pedlar, 1983; Revans, 1982) | • Involves cumulative learning, reflection on practice-based issues, group support and a focus on an individual being self-directed (Pedler, 1983; Revans, 1982; McGill and Beaty, 1992)<br>• Combines an individual's direct work experience with their learning that relates to Kolb's (1984) cycle of experiential learning utilising 'experience' and 'reflection' to 'past action'<br>• Action learning group members support and challenge the presenter through questioning and group reflection which is directed by a facilitator and guided by an action learning cycle (McGill and Beaty, 1992)<br>• Six stages are identified encompassing: the identification of the incident; describing the incident; analysing and diagnosing the incident; evaluation of theoretical frameworks and identification of further themes/action plan<br>• An essential element is the 'action' part as each presenter responds to, and reflects upon, their issue in practice after a group session; this is then reviewed in future sessions |
| Health promotion and health education (WHO, 1986; Naidoo and Wills, 2000; Scriven, 2010) | • The terms 'health promotion' and 'health education' are sometimes used interchangeably; however, health education is an aspect of health promotion work, such as creating health education patient leaflets or posters<br>• Health promotion is a broader concept and encompasses social and political processes<br>• Health promotion is a partnership between individuals, professionals, organisations and policy makers to empower individuals to make healthier choices; therefore, responsibility does not just rely with the individual (WHO, 1996; Naidoo and Wills, 2000; Scriven, 2010; Whitehead, 2018)<br>• Health promotion includes preventative programmes, such as national breast cancer screening, children's immunisation, NHS staff flu vaccination and primary school healthy eating programmes<br>• Scriven (2010) suggests five different approaches to health promotion:<br>  – medical approach: focuses on treating conditions to promote health/prevent illness<br>  – behaviour change approach: encourages behaviour change to promote good health<br>  – educational approach: emphasises role of education to develop an individual's knowledge<br>  – client-centred/empowerment approach: focuses on the individual's perspective to identify own health issues<br>  – social change approach: focuses on how society can change to facilitate health |

Additional key terms relating to teaching, supervising and supporting others are detailed in *Step 2*:

- Aim and learning objectives: *Section 2.4* and *Figure 2.2*
- SMART goals: *Section 2.4.2*
- Professional development goals: *Section 2.4.3* and *Figure 2.6*
- Professional Development Reviews (PDRs): *Section 2.4*
- Preceptorship: Preceptorship key terms, *Table 2.2*
- Appraisal: *Section 2.5*
- NMC revalidation: *Section 2.6.2*.

*Table 3.3:* Evidence-based practice and research

| Terms and key references | Further guidance |
|---|---|
| Evidence-based practice (EBP) (Cochrane, 1989; Sackett *et al.*, 1996; NHS CRD, 2019; Heaslip and Lindsay, 2019) | • An interdisciplinary approach to clinical practice that involves critically appraising the evidence available to you and applying the best available evidence to inform clinical decision-making (Cochrane, 1989; Sackett *et al.*, 1996; NHS CRD, 2019)<br>• Cochrane (1989) was the first to advocate evidence-based medicine and the national Cochrane Library database of systematic reviews is named after him<br>• Sackett *et al.* (1996) first described EBP as an integration of clinical expertise, patient values, and the best research evidence to inform the decision-making process for patient care<br>• In 1991 the Department of Health introduced the first national research strategy to provide a coordinated approach to promote EBP (DH, 1991b), which led to the following national initiatives you can access today:<br>  – NHS Centre for Reviews and Dissemination the University of York (NHS CRD, 2019): provides information on the effectiveness of treatments<br>  – NICE: see *Key national institutions and professional bodies*, above<br>  – The Cochrane Library: provides free online access to high quality systematic reviews in over 100 countries<br>  – The NIHR Research Design Service (RDS): provides expert advice to researchers on all aspects of preparing grant applications for applied research in health and social care |
| Systematic review (Higgins and Green, 2008) | • Type of literature review that involves systematic methods to collect secondary data (data which is collected by someone other than the researcher), critical appraisal of research studies (qualitative and quantitative studies) and synthesis of findings<br>• Provides a comprehensive summary of current evidence to answer a research question or defined issue |
| Qualitative and quantitative research (Creswell, 2009; Polit and Beck, 2012) | • Research studies use qualitative or quantitative designs and data collection methods; a mixed methods approach may include both qualitative and quantitative data collection methods (Creswell, 2009; Polit and Beck, 2012)<br>  – qualitative research:<br>    ◦ used to increase understanding and gain insights in relation to a defined issue, problem or research question |

*Table 3.3: (continued)*

| Terms and key references | Further guidance |
|---|---|
| | ○ data collection methods are used to explore thoughts and opinions using unstructured/semi-structured techniques<br>○ data collected usually involves narrative, photographs or video, as opposed to numerical data<br>○ sample size is usually small, to gain an in-depth analysis<br>– quantitative research:<br>○ used to quantify a problem through generating numerical data and statistics<br>○ data collected is analysed using statistical methods to formulate facts and uncover pattern<br>○ sample size needs to be larger for statistical inferences to be valid |
| Critical thinking (Cottrell, 2011) | • Complex process that involves analysis and evaluation of an issue to form a reasoned and logical judgement<br>• Essential to critically appraise and evaluate an evidence base in practice<br>• Includes self-awareness of your own views, exploration of alternative views, evaluation and analysis of evidence and interpretation of arguments and synthesis (Cottrell, 2011; Riddell, 2007)<br>• Evidence synthesis is taking an evidence base and interpreting and summarising it as a whole to develop a new perspective |

*Table 3.4: Improving quality of care*

| Terms and key references | Further guidance |
|---|---|
| Quality improvement (Ovretveit 2014; Jabbal 2017; DH, 2008) | • Systematic approach to improve the quality of healthcare services and patient outcomes through continuous testing and measuring and empowering teams (Jabbal, 2017; Ross and Naylor, 2017)<br>• The 2008 Darzi NHS Next Stage Review (DH, 2008) defined quality in the NHS according to three core areas:<br>– patient safety: do no harm to patients<br>– clinical effectiveness: promote health recovery, prevent premature death and enhance quality of life<br>– patient experiences: characterised by compassion, dignity and respect<br>• Quality assurance is the process of checking that defined healthcare standards are met, through the use of various strategies, such as clinical audits and patient satisfaction/staff feedback surveys |
| Clinical governance (Scally and Donaldson, 1998; McSherry and Pearce, 2007; Gottwald and Lansdown, 2014) | • Umbrella term which includes NHS systems and frameworks that maintain high standards and improve quality care or promote clinical excellence<br>• Traditionally, clinical governance has been described using the following seven pillars:<br>– clinical effectiveness and research<br>– audit<br>– risk management<br>– education and training<br>– patient and public involvement |

*Table 3.4: (continued)*

| Terms and key references | Further guidance |
|---|---|
| | – using information and IT<br>– staffing and staff management (Nicholls *et al.*, 2000)<br>• The CQC is responsible for assessing the performance of healthcare organisations according to KPIs (see CQC in *Key national institutions and professional bodies*, above)<br>• Frameworks/systems used by NHS organisations to improve the quality of their services and safeguard standards include: escalation pathways; clinical audits; evidence-based standards; incident reporting and devising action plans following analysis of incidents/complaints using the National Reporting and Learning System (NRLS)<br>• The NRLS is a central database of patient safety incident reports. All information submitted is analysed to identify hazards, risks and opportunities to continuously improve the safety of patient care<br>• Performance data from NHS providers is available publicly through national IT systems, which monitor trends monthly, quarterly and annually |
| Risk management (Carroll R, 2006; Kavaler, 2003) | • Involves predicting and evaluating clinical risk through analysing data from clinical incidents and complaints, along with identifying strategies to avoid and minimise future risk<br>• Involves consideration of the following three components to minimise risk:<br>– risks to patients: minimised through compliance with statutory regulations and ensuring that systems are regularly reviewed using audits and learning from critical events/complaints<br>– risks to practitioners: minimised through ensuring the safety of healthcare professionals at work by adhering to national safety legislation and the promotion of a safe working environment such as maintaining an anti-violence/bullying culture<br>– risks to the organisation minimised through maintaining high quality care, reducing risk to patients and practitioners and promoting high quality practice across services through evidence-based policies, guidelines and procedures |
| Change management models (Lewin 1947; Deming, 1950; MindTools, 2019b; NHS England, 2014) | • Describe and simplify processes when managing or implementing a change in practice<br>• Increase understanding and help structure plans to avoid error and strengthen your change process<br>• Lewin's (1947) change management model for understanding organisational change is the earliest and most widely recognised; this model includes three stages:<br>– unfreeze: determine the change required and prepare the desired change to enable movement; may involve breaking down status quo and changing existing foundations through challenging beliefs, values, attitudes, and behaviours (often the hardest stage) |

*Table 3.4: (continued)*

| Terms and key references | Further guidance |
|---|---|
| | – make changes: take action and implement the desired change; may involve embracing a new direction and proactively participating in the change<br>– refreeze: solidify the desired change that aims for permanence, a stable organisation and consistent use of tools |
| | (Lewin, 1947; MindTools, 2019b)<br>• Deming (1950) created the 'Plan, Do, Check, Act' (PDCA) quality improvement model, which later evolved into the 'Plan, Do, Study, Act' (PDSA) cycle, sometimes called the 'Deming wheel'<br>• Deming's wheel or circle is reflected in many quality improvement approaches in the NHS today<br>• The NHS Change Model (NHS England, 2014) provides a model and frameworks/guides/toolkits in relation to eight components which need to be considered when planning and implementing change:<br>1. Our shared purpose<br>2. The starting point<br>3. Spread and adoption<br>4. Improvement tools<br>5. Project and performance management<br>6. Measurement<br>7. Motivate and mobilise<br>8. Leadership by all<br>• Lean Thinking (NHS Institute of Innovation and Improvement, 2007): Current change management approach used in the NHS that embraces the following five principles:<br>– specify value:<br>○ define 'value' from the customer's perspective<br>○ value is any activity which improves the patient's health, wellbeing and experience<br>– identify the value stream or patient journey:<br>○ core set of actions required to deliver value for patients<br>○ standardise the pathway<br>– make the process and value flow:<br>○ align healthcare processes to facilitate smooth flow of patients and information<br>○ drive out waste<br>– let the customer pull:<br>○ the customer should pull products or services as needed<br>○ deliver care on demand with the resources needed<br>– pursue perfection:<br>○ develop and amend processes continuously to pursue the ideal<br>○ perfection is the 'benchmark' |

*Table 3.4: (continued)*

| Terms and key references | Further guidance |
|---|---|
| Clinical audit (Burgess, 2011; Health Quality Improvement Partnership (HQIP), 2019; NHS England, 2019b) | • A quality improvement process that aims to improve patient care and outcomes by methodically reviewing the delivery of care to ensure that best practice is being delivered (Burgess, 2011; HQIP, 2019; NHS England, 2019b)<br>• Involves evaluation of a clinical service using a defined standard<br>• Not just a data collection exercise, as changes may be implemented following a clinical audit (if indicated) and further monitoring should confirm an improvement using a cyclical process<br>• The National Clinical Audit and Patient Outcomes Programme (NCAPOP) audits are commissioned and managed on behalf of NHS England by the Healthcare Quality Improvement Partnership (HQIP, 2019); the programme includes over 30 national audits relating to commonly-occurring conditions. Some NCAPOP audit examples:<br>  – Falls and Fragility Fracture Audit Programme (FFFAP) (includes national hip fracture database)<br>  – Myocardial Ischaemia National Audit Project (MINAP)<br>  – National Adult Diabetes Audit (NDA)<br>  – National Audit of Care at the End of Life (NACEL)<br>  – National Audit of Dementia (NAD)<br>  – National Asthma and COPD Audit Programme (NACAP) |
| Quality standards (NICE, 2016; 2019) | • Gives you a set of statements to help improve quality and measure progress<br>• NICE (2019) sets evidence-based standards for day-to-day clinical practice (see NICE in *Key national institutions and professional bodies*, above)<br>• NICE (2016) provides an overview of the quality standard development process and a guide for developing quality standards, and the CQC uses quality standards to help identify/define good quality care |
| Protocol, policy and guidelines (NHS England, 2019c; NHS Wales, 2006) | • Protocol: agreed framework or structure outlining care that will be delivered to patients in a defined area of practice<br>• Policy: official written statement detailing the specific action to be taken in a particular situation that is contractually binding<br>• Guideline: methodical series of statements that help healthcare practitioners make decisions about care in specific clinical circumstances |
| Care plan (Orlando, 1961; Wilson *et al.*, 2018) | • Orlando (1961) conceived the 'Nursing Process' theory that underpins our care plans and practice today<br>• The Nursing Process was devised to be cyclical, dynamic and continuous, problem-solving and goal-directed, patient-centred and collaborative, methodical and systematic, and globally applicable (Orlando, 1961)<br>• Care plans usually involve the following four key stages:<br>  – assessment<br>  – goal planning<br>  – implementation plan<br>  – evaluation<br>• The aim of a care plan is to ensure the following:<br>  – patients' needs are met using a holistic approach<br>  – care delivered is safe, evidence-based, correct and continuous<br>  – nursing care delivered/not delivered is recorded<br>  – effectiveness of care is recorded through nursing evaluation |

*Table 3.5: Management and leadership*

| Terms and key references | Further guidance |
|---|---|
| Management and leadership (Barr and Dowding, 2019; Gopee and Galloway, 2017; Jones and Bennett, 2018) | The key differences between management and leadership are summarised below: <br>• Management is a set of processes that keeps a complicated system of people/technology running smoothly <br>• Managers have people who work for them and they control and direct people/resources according to established principles, which includes planning, budgeting, organising, staffing, controlling and problem-solving <br>• Leadership is a set of processes that leads others towards a common goal by creating, adapting or changing circumstances <br>• Leaders define what the future should look like and inspire/motivate others to share their vision and make it happen by overcoming obstacles <br><br>(Barr and Dowding, 2019; Gopee and Galloway, 2017; Jones and Bennett, 2018) <br><br>There are various leadership styles that have been identified, such as: <br>• Authoritative leadership: <br>  – top-down power dynamic <br>  – focuses on the 'boss' with a clear distinction between the leader and their followers/workers <br>  – leader holds all authority and responsibility <br>  – leader reaches decisions without consulting, then communicates to subordinates expecting prompt implementation <br>  – work environment is inflexible <br>  – focus on efficiency <br>  – may create a climate of fear and no room for discussion <br>• Paternalistic leadership: <br>  – leader shows concern for followers/workers <br>  – leader receives trust and loyalty from followers/workers <br>  – workers expected to become totally committed to what the leader believes <br>  – built on solid relationship between leader and workers <br>  – leader may identify favourites such as workers who are keener to follow them, and exclude those who are not <br>• Democratic leadership: <br>  – power dynamic consists of communications from top down, and down up <br>  – focuses on workers' contributions, contrasting to autocratic leadership <br>  – democratic leader has overall responsibility but may delegate authority to others <br>  – leader shares decision-making abilities with others <br>  – practises social equality, as all humans play a part in the group's decisions <br>  – deemed the most effective leadership style as it creates higher productivity, better contributions from group members and increased group morale |

**Table 3.5:** *(continued)*

| Terms and key references | Further guidance |
|---|---|
| | • Laissez-faire leadership: |
| |   – allows self-rule, as power to make decisions is given to followers/workers |
| |   – complete freedom for all to make decisions concerning the completion of work |
| |   – laissez-faire leader may offer guidance and support when requested |
| |   – followers need to be highly skilled, experienced and educated |
| | • Transactional leadership: |
| |   – maintains the status quo |
| |   – not looking to change the future, cf. transformational leadership |
| |   – involves an exchange process and rewards for carrying out leader's orders |
| |   – leader promotes compliance through rewards and punishments |
| |   – focuses on supervision, organisation and performance |
| |   – not concerned with the wellbeing of workers, cf. transformational leadership |
| | • Transformational leadership: |
| |   – focuses on initiating change through motivational transformational leaders |
| |   – motivates others to do more than they originally intended and think possible |
| |   – sets challenging expectations to achieve higher performance |
| |   – empowers followers/workers to work to the best of their ability |
| | (Barr and Dowding, 2019; Gopee and Galloway, 2017; Jones and Bennett, 2018; MindTools, 2019a) |
| | The Healthcare Leadership Model (NHS Leadership Academy, 2019) is made up of nine leadership dimensions: |
| | • Inspiring shared purpose: values a service ethos and aims to improve services and patient care |
| | • Leading with care: focuses on personal qualities for leaders and the unique qualities/needs of a team |
| | • Evaluating information: seeks out information and makes effective plans for improvement/change |
| | • Connecting our service: understands how people, services and organisations interconnect/interact |
| | • Sharing the vision: communicates vision of the future that is achievable |
| | • Engaging the team: demonstrates that all contributions are valued, to deliver outcomes and improve services |
| | • Holding to account: agree clear performance goals and quality indicators |
| | • Developing capability: build capability to enable people to meet future challenges |
| | • Influencing for results: have a positive impact on people and build collaboration |

*Table 3.5: (continued)*

| Terms and key references | Further guidance |
|---|---|
| Team roles<br>(Ellis and Bach; 2015; Belbin, 2015) | Belbin's (2015) 'Self-Perception Inventory' categorises a person's behavioural strengths/weaknesses under 'team roles' to increase their self-awareness in the workplace (Belbin, 2015). The nine Belbin (2015) team roles and traits are summarised below:<br>• Resource investigator: outgoing; enthusiastic; explores opportunities and develops contacts; might be over-optimistic and can lose interest once initial enthusiasm has passed<br>• Team worker: co-operative; perceptive and diplomatic; listens and averts friction; can be indecisive in crunch situations and tends to avoid confrontation<br>• Co-ordinator: mature; confident; identifies talent; clarifies goals; can be seen as manipulative and might offload their own share of the work<br>• Plant: creative; imaginative; free-thinking; generates ideas and solves difficult problems; may ignore incidentals and be too preoccupied to communicate effectively<br>• Monitor evaluator: sober; strategic and discerning; sees all options and judges accurately; sometimes lacks the drive and ability to inspire others and can be overly critical<br>• Specialist: single-minded; self-starting and dedicated; provides specialist knowledge and skills; tends to contribute on a narrow front and can dwell on the technicalities<br>• Shaper: challenging; dynamic; thrives on pressure; has the drive and courage to overcome obstacles; can be prone to provocation and may sometimes offend people's feelings<br>• Implementer: practical; reliable; efficient; turns ideas into actions and organises work that needs to be done; can be a bit inflexible and slow to respond to new possibilities<br>• Completer finisher: painstaking; conscientious; anxious; searches out errors; polishes and perfects; can be inclined to worry unduly and be reluctant to delegate |

## WHAT TO DO NEXT

1. Prior to interviews, review key professional terms relating to a specific role/course.
2. Reflect on areas of interest in practice and identify local projects you could collaborate with. Network with local/national colleagues and specialist leads to share ideas, resources and experiences.
3. Critically review the evidence base relating to your area of interest and identify similarities, differences and gaps in the evidence base.
4. Review organisational structures and frameworks defined by government, legal and professional bodies. Ensure future service improvement projects or research studies adhere to national regulations, frameworks and guidelines.

5. Review national ethical and consent procedures devised by the UK Health Research Authority (HRA) and the principles of the Mental Health Act (2007). Seek authorisation and consent from your line manager prior to commencing local projects. Obtain formal consent from local managers and research leads prior to conducting a research study in a clinical area or community setting.
6. Visit your local media and communications department and review the corporate standards it sets for internal and external communications. Adhere to employer media and communication standards when publishing work or producing marketing/educational materials.
7. Share and disseminate your project work, where appropriate, through networking, conference presentations, social media and publishing articles.

## REFERENCES AND FURTHER READING

Barr, J. and Dowding, L. (2019) *Leadership in Health Care,* 4th edition. Sage.

Belbin (2015) Team Role Theory – Belbin Team Roles (online). Available at: www.belbin.com/about/belbin-team-roles/ [accessed 10 December 2019]

Bradley, L. and Rees, C. (2003) Reducing nutritional risk in hospital: the red tray. *Nursing Standard,* **17**(26): 33–37.

Bulman, C., Lathlean, J. and Gobbi, M. (2012) The concept of reflection in nursing: qualitative findings on student and teacher perspectives. *Nurse Education Today,* **32**: 8–13.

Bulman, C. and Schutz, S. (eds) (2013) *Reflective Practice in Nursing,* 5th edition. John Wiley & Sons Ltd.

Burgess, R. (2011) *New Principles of Best Practice in Clinical Audit.* Health Quality Improvement Partnership.

Caldicott Committee (1997) *Report on the Review of Patient-Identifiable Information.* Crown Copyright. Available at: https://webarchive.nationalarchives.gov.uk/20130124064947/http://www.dh.gov.uk/prod_consum_dh/groups/dh_digitalassets/@dh/@en/documents/digitalasset/dh_4068404.pdf [accessed 10 December 2019]

Care Quality Commission (2013) *Supporting Information and Guidance: supporting effective clinical supervision.* CQC. Available at: https://cqc.org.uk/sites/default/files/documents/20130625_800734_v1_00_supporting_information-effective_clinical_supervision_for_publication.pdf [accessed 10 December 2019]

Carroll, R. (2006) *Risk Management Handbook for Health Care Organizations: risk management in health care – the essentials.* Jossey-Bass.

Cochrane, A.L. (1989) *Effectiveness and Efficiency: random reflections on health services.* Wiley Blackwell.

Cottrell, S. (2011) *Critical Thinking Skills: developing effective analysis and argument.* Palgrave Macmillan.

Creswell, J.W. (2009) *Research Design: qualitative, quantitative, and mixed methods approaches.* Sage Publications.

Data Protection Act (2018) The Stationery Office. Available at: www.legislation.gov.uk/ukpga/2018/12/contents/enacted [accessed 10 December 2019]

Deming, W.E. (1950) *Plan-Do-Check-Act (PDCA)* (online). Available at: www.mindtools.com/pages/article/newPPM_89.htm [accessed 10 December 2019]

Department of Health (1990) *National Health Service and Community Care Act.* The Stationery Office.

Department of Health (1991a) *The Patient's Charter.* The Stationery Office.

Department of Health (1991b) *Research for Health: a research and development strategy for the NHS.* HMSO.

Department of Health (2008) *High Quality Care For All: NHS next stage review final report.* The Stationery Office. Available at: https://assets.publishing.service.gov.uk/government/uploads/system/uploads/attachment_data/file/228836/7432.pdf [accessed 10 December 2019]

de Silva, D. (2015) *No. 24 What's getting in the way? Barriers to improvement in the NHS.* The Health Foundation.

Ellis, P. and Bach, S. (2015) *Leadership, Management and Team Working in Nursing (Transforming Nursing Practice Series),* 2nd edition. Sage.

Gibbs, G. (1988) *Learning by Doing: a guide to teaching and learning methods.* Further Education Unit, Oxford Polytechnic.

Gopee, N. and Galloway, J. (2017) *Leadership and Management in Healthcare,* 3rd edition. Sage.

Gottwald, M. and Lansdown, G. (2014) *Clinical Governance: improving the quality of healthcare for patients and service users.* Open University Press.

Health and Safety Executive (2018) *Work Related Stress, Depression or Anxiety.* Crown Copyright.

Health and Social Care Act (2012) DH.

Health Quality Improvement Partnership (2019) *The National Clinical Audit Programme*. HQIP. Available at: www.hqip.org.uk/a-z-of-nca/#. XMBW8EiIrIU [accessed 10 December 2019]

Heaslip, V. and Lindsay, B. (2019) *Research and Evidence-Based Practice: for nursing, health and social care students*. Lantern Publishing.

#hellomynameis campaign. Available at: https://hellomynameis.org.uk/ [accessed 10 December 2019]

Higgins, J. and Green, S. (2008) *Cochrane Handbook for Systematic Reviews of Interventions: the Cochrane Collaboration*. John Wiley & Sons.

Hollis, S. (2011) Using red jugs to improve hydration. *Nursing Times*, 107: 28.

Jabbal, J. (2017) *Embedding a Culture of Quality Improvement*. The King's Fund. Available at: www.kingsfund.org.uk/sites/default/ files/2017-11/Embedding-culture-QI-Kings-Fund-November-2017.pdf [accessed 10 December 2019]

Johns, C. (2000) *Becoming a Reflective Practitioner*. Blackwell.

Johnson, J. *et al.* (2016) Resilience to emotional distress in response to failure, error or mistakes: a systematic review. *Clinical Psychology Review*, 52: 19–42.

Jones, L. and Bennett, C.L. (2018) *Leadership: for nursing, health and social care students*. Lantern Publishing.

Kavaler, F. (2003) *Risk Management in Health Care Institutions: a strategic approach*, 2nd revised edition. Jones and Bartlett Publishers.

Khan, K. *et al.* (2003) Five steps to conducting a systematic review. *Journal of the Royal Society of Medicine*, 96(3): 118–121.

Kirrane, C. (1993) Informed help wanted on making post-basic education choices. *Nursing Times*, 89(7): 12.

Kolb, D.A. (1984) *Experiential Learning: experience as the source of learning and development*. Prentice-Hall.

Lewin, K. (1947) Frontiers in group dynamics: concept, method and reality in social science; social equilibria and social change. *Human Relations*, 1(1): 5–41.

Marshall, P.A. (2006) *Informed Consent in International Health Research*. University of California Press.

McGill, I. and Beaty, L. (1992) *Action Learning: a practitioner's guide*. Kogan Page.

McSherry, R. and Pearce, P. (2007) *Clinical Governance: a guide to implementation for healthcare professionals*. Blackwell Publishing.

Medical Research Council (2019) Online tool and guidance on consent. MRC. Available at: www.hra.nhs.uk/planning-and-improving-research/best-practice/informing-participants-and-seeking-consent/ [accessed 10 December 2019]

Medicines and Healthcare products Regulatory Agency (2015) *Best Practice Guidance on Patient Information Leaflets*. Available at: https://assets.publishing.service.gov.uk/government/uploads/system/uploads/attachment_data/file/328405/Best_practice_guidance_on_patient_information_leaflets.pdf [accessed 10 December 2019]

Mental Health Act (2007) The Stationery Office. Available at: www.legislation.gov.uk/ukpga/2007/12/pdfs/ukpga_20070012_en.pdf [accessed 10 December 2019]

MindTools (2019a) *Leadership Styles: choosing the right approach for the situation*. Available at: www.mindtools.com/pages/article/newLDR_84.htm [accessed 10 December 2019]

MindTools (2019b) *Lewin's Change Management Model: understanding the three stages of change*. Available at: www.mindtools.com/pages/article/newPPM_94.htm [accessed 10 December 2019]

Naidoo, J. and Wills, J. (2000) *Health Promotion: foundations for practice*. Bailliere Tindall.

National Institute for Health and Care Excellence (2016) *Health and Social Care Directorate: Quality Standards – Process Guide*. NICE. Available at: www.nice.org.uk/Media/Default/Standards-and-indicators/Quality-standards/quality-standards-process-guide.pdf [accessed 11 December 2019]

National Institute for Health and Care Excellence (2019) *Standards and Indicators*. NICE. Available at: www.nice.org.uk/standards-and-indicators [accessed 11 December 2019]

NHS Centre for Reviews (NHS CRD) (2019) *University of York Centre for Reviews and Dissemination*. Available at: www.york.ac.uk/crd/ [accessed 10 December 2019]

NHS England (2014) *The Change Model Guide*. Sustainable Improvement Team: NHS England. Available at: www.england.nhs.uk/wp-content/uploads/2018/04/change-model-guide-v5.pdf [accessed 10 December 2019]

NHS England (2019a) *The NHS Long Term Plan*. Available at: www.longtermplan.nhs.uk [accessed 2 January 2020]

NHS England (2019b) *Clinical Audit*. Available at: www.england.nhs.uk/clinaudit/ [accessed 10 December 2019]

NHS England (2019c) *Our Policies and Procedures*. Available at: www.england.nhs.uk/contact-us/pub-scheme/pol-proc/ [accessed 10 December 2019]

NHS Institute of Innovation and Improvement (2007) *Going Lean in the NHS*. Available at: www.england.nhs.uk/improvement-hub/wp-content/uploads/sites/44/2017/11/Going-Lean-in-the-NHS.pdf [accessed 10 December 2019]

NHS Leadership Academy (2019) *Healthcare Leadership Model*. Available at: www.leadershipacademy.nhs.uk/resources/healthcare-leadership-model/ [accessed 10 December 2019]

NHS Wales (2006) *Using Protocols, Standards, Policies and Guidelines to Enhance Confidence and Career Development*. Available at: www.wales.nhs.uk/sitesplus/documents/861/Wipp%20Using%20Protocols%2Cstandards%2C%20policies%20and%20guidelines.pdf [accessed 11 December 2019]

Nicholls, S. *et al.* (2000) Clinical governance: its origins and its foundations. *Clinical Performance and Quality Healthcare*, 8(3): 172–8.

Nightingale, F. (1859) *A Contribution to the Sanitary History of the British Army During the Late War with Russia*. John W. Parker & Sons.

Nightingale, F. (1863) *Notes on Hospitals*. Longman, Green, Roberts & Green.

Nursing and Midwifery Council (2008) *Standards to Support Learning and Assessment in Practice: NMC standards for mentors, practice teachers and teachers*. NMC.

Nursing and Midwifery Council (2015) *Guidance on Using Social Media Responsibly*. NMC.

Nursing and Midwifery Council (2018a) *Realising Professionalism: standards for education and training. Part 2: Standards for student supervision and assessment*. Available at: www.nmc.org.uk/globalassets/sitedocuments/education-standards/student-supervision-assessment.pdf [accessed 11 December 2019]

Nursing and Midwifery Council (2018b) *The Code: professional standards of practice and behaviour for nurses, midwives and nursing associates*. Available at: www.nmc.org.uk/globalassets/sitedocuments/nmc-publications/nmc-code.pdf [accessed 11 December 2019]

Oelofsen, N. (2012) *Developing Reflective Practice: a guide for students and practitioners of health and social care*. Lantern Publishing.

Orlando, I.J. (1961) *The Dynamic Nurse–Patient Relationship*. G.P. Putnam's Sons: Penguin Adult.

Ovretveit, J. (2014) *Evaluating Improvement and Implementation for Health*. Open University Press.

Pedler, M. (1983) *Action Learning in Practice*. Gower Publishing.

Pick, A. *et al.* (2013) Informed consent in clinical research. *Nursing Standard*, **27(49)**: 44–47.

Polit, D.F. and Beck, C.T. (2012) *Nursing Research: generating and assessing evidence for nursing practice*. Wolters Kluwer Health/ Lippincott Williams & Wilkins.

Pollock, A. *et al.* (2017) A systematic review of evidence relating to clinical supervision for nurses, midwives and allied health professionals. *Journal of Advanced Nursing*, **73(8)**: 1825–1837.

Revans, R. (1982) *The Origins and Growth of Action Learning*. Chartwell-Bratt Ltd.

Riddell, T. (2007) Critical assumptions: thinking critically about critical thinking. *Journal of Nursing Education*, **46(3)**: 121–6.

Ross, S. and Naylor, C. (2017) *Quality Improvement in Mental Health*. The King's Fund. Available at: www.kingsfund.org.uk/sites/default/ files/field/field_publication_file/Quality_improvement_mental_health_ Kings_Fund_July_2017_0.pdf [accessed 11 December 2019]

Royal College of Nursing (2019a) *Safe and Effective Staffing: the real picture*. RCN. Available at: www.rcn.org.uk/professional- development/publications/pub-006195 [accessed 11 December 2019]

Royal College of Nursing (2019b) *Staffing for Safe and Effective Care: Nursing on the Brink*. RCN. Available at: www.rcn.org.uk/ professional-development/publications/pdf-007025 [accessed 2 January 2020]

Sackett, D.L. *et al.* (1996) Evidence based medicine: what it is and what it isn't. *British Medical Journal*, **312**: 71.

Scally, G. and Donaldson, L.J. (1998) Clinical governance and the drive for quality improvement in the new NHS in England. *British Medical Journal*, **317**: 61–65.

Schön, D. (1991) *The Reflective Practitioner*. Ashgate Publishing.

Scriven, A. (2010) *Promoting Health: a practical guide*. Bailliere Tindall Elsevier.

Whitehead, D. (2018) Exploring health promotion and health education in nursing. *Nursing Standard*, **33(8)**: 38–44.

Wilson, B. *et al.* (2018) *Care Planning: a guide for nurses*. Routledge: Taylor and Francis Group.

World Health Organization (1986) *The Ottawa Charter*. WHO. Available at: www.who.int/healthpromotion/conferences/previous/ ottawa/en/ [accessed 11 December 2019]

# STEP 4

# COMPLETE A STRONG APPLICATION AND PERSONAL STATEMENT

*"An unnecessary love of the thesaurus may have exactly the opposite effect."*
Daniel Oppenheimer, author of *Consequences of erudite vernacular utilized irrespective of necessity: problems with using long words needlessly* (2006)

## 4.1 THE IMPORTANCE OF A STRONG APPLICATION AND PERSONAL STATEMENT

The importance of submitting a strong application cannot be underestimated when applying for a job or course to support your career progression. The narrative you submit on an application form, particularly within your personal statement and curriculum vitae (CV), can make the difference between being called to an interview and your application being rejected. The more applicants there are for a post, the more competitive the shortlisting and interview process will become, especially when you are applying for highly sought-after roles and courses that align to a career pathway (see *Table 1.4*).

Reputable employers prefer to re-advertise a job or career opportunity rather than take a chance on appointing the wrong person, so even if you are the only applicant for a post or course, you should still make just as much effort as if there were several applicants. Putting it bluntly, most managers are aiming to avoid having to performance-manage staff later, or wasting course fees on someone who does not practically apply what they have learnt in the clinical field. If there are doubts, they would rather not appoint.

### 4.1.1 Clear and concise language is key

The phrase "Erudite vernacular utilized irrespective of necessity" in the title of Oppenheimer's (2006) research paper is a humorous example of excessively complicated narrative that basically means 'using long words needlessly'. Oppenheimer, a professor of psychology and public affairs, examined the complexity of words used by undergraduates in their essays and personal statements for admission to college. Undergraduates admitted to increasing the complexity of their vocabulary to "*give the impression of intelligence*" when applying for university. Oppenheimer's study explores the extent to which this strategy is effective, and he invites us to consider our language to avoid needless complexity, which may give the impression you are feeling insecure in your abilities.

Oppenheimer acknowledges that his findings are not generalisable to all writers, as there are times when a longer word will enhance a text. However, his conclusions are helpful when considering your language on future application forms, CVs and personal statements, which may have word limits. The language you use will affect the overall impression you are conveying to recruiters and the aim is not to show off your "*love of the thesaurus*". It is best to use words that you understand which are clear, concise and logical. Do not use generic healthcare terms, such as 'evidence-based practice', 'clinical governance' and 'transformational leadership', unless you can provide evidence of understanding and practical application.

### 4.1.2 Your CV and personal statement are marketing 'you'

Never rely solely on your past experience to secure an interview. Your personal statement and CV are of equal importance, as they differentiate you from other candidates who may have experienced similar roles or attained a similar standard of professional development to you. Always make an effort when completing your application form, personal statement and CV. Do not just write a few rushed sentences the night before, or present bullet points enthusing about your compassion towards others without actual examples. Personal statements and CVs are important marketing tools showcasing your transferable skills, whilst concisely conveying to the interviewer why you are the right person for the role/course on offer. They enable applicants to set themselves apart from other candidates through highlighting personal achievements and awards (see *Step 7*).

This chapter provides guidance to support your future applications and offers practical tips to help you complete future application forms, personal statements, CVs and personal professional portfolios. The general advice presented may be used throughout your career.

# 4.2 YOUR APPLICATION FORM

## 4.2.1 *Always check shortlisting criteria*

Staff preparing for future roles or course applications should note that there is always a minimum amount of experience and minimum qualifications required for any job or academic programme, and these will be detailed in the person specification or course entry criteria. For example, six months' post-registration oncology experience may be required, prior to applying for an employer-funded chemotherapy course; a minimum of one year's post-registration experience for a band 6 role; or completion of a Nurse Prescribing Master's module for a band 7 advanced nurse/midwife practitioner role. I have supported many staff over the years who were frustrated as they did not meet the shortlisting criteria. Some did not realise this until they had downloaded the application form!

A few simple tips relating to shortlisting are presented below:

- Review job descriptions and person specifications for shortlisting criteria well in advance, by downloading related documents from national job websites or employer sites (see *Where to find jobs* in *Section 4.2*).
- There will be a section for 'essential' and 'desirable' person specifications and you cannot apply for a role if you do not meet the 'essential' criteria. The more 'desirables' stipulated that you already have, the stronger your application and suitability for the post.
- Contact local HR advisers and line managers to obtain accurate shortlisting criteria if online job descriptions and person specifications are not clear.
- If you contact individuals who already work in a role for information, make sure that you check the data is correct and up to date. The shortlisting criteria for a new applicant may be very different in comparison to someone who has worked in a role for many years.
- Review university websites or contact course leads/administrators directly by phone/email for prerequisite course entry criteria.
- If you completed courses years ago, or studied in another country, you may be unsure of the academic credits awarded at the time. UK universities will request an academic transcription from your previous course lead, which can take time if past lecturers have left.

## 4.2.2 *Where to find jobs*

There are a variety of places to look for nursing and midwifery jobs across the UK. NHS employers advertise using online recruitment sites, such as NHS Jobs, NHS Scotland Recruitment and Healthcarejobs.ie. UK midwifery students and RMs can enrol on 'MidwivesJobs', the official RCM jobs board. Private sector healthcare employers often advertise on more generic sites, such as Indeed. Additionally, employers may place adverts in popular national nursing journals, local job centres, newspapers and on noticeboards within institutions.

Look out for local and national recruitment events too, which are usually advertised using online media. You can meet potential employers and clinical staff face to face at these events, and they will offer informal visits (see *Section 1.2.6*). The RCN and 'Nursing Times Careers Live' offer several recruitment events across different UK locations throughout the year, aimed at students and newly qualified staff.

### Some useful job websites

NHS Jobs: www.jobs.nhs.uk/
NHS Scotland Recruitment: https://jobs.scot.nhs.uk/
Healthcarejobs.ie: www.healthcarejobs.ie/
MidwivesJobs: https://jobs.midwives.co.uk/
Indeed: www.indeed.co.uk/
RCN Bulletin Jobs: www.rcnbulletinjobs.co.uk/
Nursing Times Careers Live: https://live.nursingtimes.net/

### 4.2.3  Don't compare yourself to others!

Whilst offering career advice to staff over the years, I have met many individuals who were limited by their lack of confidence. They doubted their own abilities or compared themselves unfavourably to a colleague, which led them to withdraw their application or not to apply at all. Remember, all candidates have an equal chance of being appointed if they are shortlisted. Success depends on a strong application and a person's interview performance on the day. It is always unwise to make a decision on whether or not to apply for a position based on preconceived ideas of who you think will be successful.

### 4.2.4  Do what it says on the application form and don't go off-piste!

An application form, CV and personal statement will inevitably become interconnected. Your CV and personal statement may inform each other, along with the 'supporting information' or 'additional information' section in your application form. Some application forms request that you upload your personal statement and CVs as separate documents, whereas others will not expect additional documents.

### Follow instructions to the letter

It is extremely important that you read each section of an application form and follow the instructions given. You must adhere to what is actually being requested and not stray from this guidance. Over the years, I have been asked to critically review many student and staff applications before they submit them. There are always individuals who decide to add additional information that is not being asked for, which is a waste of words when there may be set word limits. If an application form requests a 150-word personal statement to summarise how you will personally benefit from a course, then the person shortlisting will not want to read 120 words summarising a previous academic course. In summary, never go off-piste! It annoys those who have to shortlist numerous applications and jeopardises your chances of being called to an interview.

### Adhere to the closing date

All job adverts will state the closing date for applications. Always upload online application documents, or send postal applications, within the time parameter set. Damaged computers, or internet access being down, will not be accepted as an excuse for late applications. Nowadays, the majority of applications are uploaded using online tracking systems that make it impossible for late submissions to be accepted.

### Have a personal statement and CV ready to go when needed

It is always good to be prepared by having a personal statement and CV template ready to go whenever you need it. They should both be 'active' documents that you can update whenever you achieve professional or academic milestones.

## 4.2.5 Presentation matters

All application documents, whether online or paper, will have space for free-form text to type your own words. It is this open narrative that sets you apart from other applicants. Sloppy grammar, spelling mistakes and poor presentation do not give the right impression.

---

**KEY TIP**

- Remember, first impressions count, as recruiters often spend only a short amount of time scanning each application form, covering letter, CV and personal statement.

---

Additional tips are presented below to enhance the standard of presentation within your application.

## Checks

- Always use online spelling and grammatical error checks, but don't rely on them.
- Review your application several times before uploading or posting documents.
- Ask colleagues, friends or family to proofread your application documents prior to submission.
- Unfortunately, we are not at the stage nationally when you can upload visual or verbal applications in healthcare. Therefore, if you are a person with dyslexia you may find literacy and 'text-to-speak' software helpful, which you can access through the British Dyslexia Association website.

## Narrative content

- Don't try to be too clever, using unfamiliar words that you don't fully comprehend. It is better to use simple and concise language that you understand.
- You can use the words 'I' and 'my' in your application, as it is about you as a person. If you can write in the third person in places instead, then do so; for example: 'Collaborating with the MDT team led to an increased awareness of roles across services…'.

## Format and structure

- Use consistent formatting throughout, e.g. margins, bullet points, tables and font.
- Use a simple font style, such as Arial or Times New Roman, and consistent font size, e.g. minimum size 11 points for main text and slightly larger fonts for headings/sub-headings.

- Use bold for headings to make them stand out.
- Avoid colour or pictures and aim to keep the tone simple, professional and streamlined.
- Avoid abbreviations as they may confuse a reader.
- You may use bulleted lists and tables to align content in your application or CV; however, your personal supporting statement should contain themed and flowing paragraphs with no bullets. A personal statement should be written like an essay, with a clear introduction, a few main themed paragraphs, and a conclusion summarising future goals (see the example personal statements in *Section 4.3*).
- A standard CV should be an appropriate length, usually two pages of A4, with good amounts of spacing to enhance presentation (see CVs, *Section 4.4*).

### 4.2.6  Recruiters take account of past experience and initiative

It is important to remember that recruiters will take account of any previous or current employment, experiences or initiatives that may, or may not, be related to nursing/midwifery. I know of several students who started as a band 6 on qualification, as their past experiences were recognised, or they had the initiative and drive to successfully line up a band 6 academic research internship post.

Gerard Mawhinney, one of my ex-students, did both. He ran his own business before commencing a master's in nursing, and demonstrated key transferable leadership skills on his application and during interview. While preparing his dissertation: 'Can the introduction of personalised video consent technology achieve high patient satisfaction with the preoperative consent giving process?' he networked with key national research bodies and medical/nursing leads in a hospital Trust. Gerard became a band 6 research nurse on qualification and immediately worked towards securing a band 7 spinal research post. Collaborating with key staff enabled him to gain support to conduct a research study examining the use of video consent in theatres (Mawhinney *et al.*, 2019). Gerard was awarded a fellowship in surgical care practice as a band 7 within a year qualified, which allowed him to take up a role as a surgical care practitioner trainee band 8 in Spinal Surgery, two years post-registration.

Nowadays, there are more career opportunities available to nurses and midwives than ever before, as long as you are ambitious, driven and willing to invest time and energy pursuing your goals.

### 4.2.7  Declaring disabilities

It is unlawful for an employer to discriminate against you at any stage of the hiring process for having a disability. Following the Equality Act (2010), prospective employers are not allowed to ask candidates any disability-related questions on application forms. Employers can, however, make 'limited enquiries' to establish if reasonable adjustments would be needed at interview or when carrying out your role.

If you are unsure whether to disclose a disability, you may find the *Disability Rights Handbook* helpful to inform your decision (Greaves, 2019). An HR adviser will also be able to give you confidential advice on how to manage potential declarations or challenging conversations. Remember that many UK healthcare employers have signed up to become 'Disability Confident Committed', which demonstrates their commitment to promoting opportunities for people with disabilities.

Ultimately, the decision to disclose a disability is yours; however, it is important to note that if you opt **not to disclose a disability to an employer**, and you encounter issues later whilst performing your role, you may not be protected by the Equality Act (2010). In summary, your employer cannot be deemed to have acted in a discriminatory fashion towards you, if they were unaware of your disability.

### 4.2.8  References

If you are successful following an interview, you are usually informed by the lead interviewer by phone/email and will be asked whether you wish to accept their provisional offer. Following your verbal acceptance, a formal offer letter will be forthcoming, pending the outcome of your health assessment and references. As part of an application process, you will be asked to provide the name and contact details of two referees on your application form. Make sure that you give up-to-date contact details for each referee, otherwise you risk delaying your formal offer.

#### How do you select referees?

You should not choose a relative or close friend to be your referee. Your referee should know you in a professional or academic capacity, depending on what you are applying for. Referees should have appropriate professional/academic qualifications for the opportunity being applied for.

**Clinical references** are requested when you apply for any RN/RM post in a clinical/community setting in the UK. The clinical referee will usually comment on areas such as:

- your suitability to care for others
- use of a person-centred approach
- communication skills
- ability to work within a team
- flexibility and ability to work under pressure
- reliability and willingness to direct your own learning.

A clinical referee should be in a higher banding or senior position to you, to be able to comment on your performance and character, e.g. a registered practice supervisor for an NQN/NQM or a team leader, deputy or manager for an experienced RN/RM.

If you apply for a course, scholarship, secondment or internship, the recruiter will usually insist on an academic referee to ensure you meet any future academic standards required. **Academic references** are usually provided by a past or current course/module lead, academic/personal tutor or practice supervisor. If a past tutor has left university, then a programme lead or another lecturer should access a course transcription that details your previous results. However, be aware that this takes time, especially if a request is made over the summer period.

An academic referee will be asked to comment on areas such as:

- previous commitment to your studies
- your average marks
- your academic achievements
- your academic suitability to complete whatever is being offered.

If you are newly qualified, you usually choose one clinical referee (a practice supervisor from a previous placement) and one academic referee (usually your personal tutor or academic supervisor).

If you have worked for a healthcare agency during your training, you may choose a relevant referee from past work experiences, as long as you have worked with the person long enough for them to act as a clinical referee.

Most referees need to have worked with you within the last year (depending on reference guidance). An 8–12-week placement with a practice supervisor, who has assessed your competencies, is absolutely fine; a couple of days would not be deemed sufficient.

Some post-registration course applications request 'the most recent line manager' as your referee and their support will be mandatory, as services may be affected by your attendance on study days.

## Always ask for permission

Always gain permission from potential referees before you submit their details on application forms. It is common courtesy to ask the person whether they are happy to act as your referee, before you put their name forward. You should also inform referees when you have applied for posts so that they can expect a reference request. I was once contacted by an HR department six years after leaving an institution, to give a reference for someone, which was inappropriate; firstly, because they hadn't asked me, and secondly, because my reference would not be valid after a six-year time lapse. If the person had contacted me in the first place, I would have informed them of this to prevent any unnecessary delays.

Asking a person to be your referee gives them an opportunity to refuse, as they may feel they cannot provide you with a good reference. It is standard practice for a potential referee to inform you if they are not happy to provide a positive reference, as that allows you time to ask someone else.

As a student, if you come across an exceptionally supportive practice supervisor who gives you excellent feedback during second/third-year placements, always ask them at the time: "*Would you be happy to provide a future reference for me when I eventually apply for jobs?*" You will be consolidating your case management and leadership skills during this time, which they can comment on. Often practice supervisors are thrilled that you have asked them to act as your referee. Keep in contact with them after you leave an area, in case they move on to another role elsewhere.

### 4.2.9  A covering letter

#### When do you use a covering letter?

A covering letter may be used if there are no current job adverts out and you wish to be considered for a future post, or you are proactively trying to find out about future opportunities through a charity or external institution.

This proactive process is sometimes termed 'applying speculatively' to an employer, person or institution.

The overall aim of a covering letter is to interest a person enough for them to read your CV and to offer you a future opportunity. The language in your letter should make you stand out and persuade the reader that you are a person worth meeting.

### How do I present my covering letter?

A covering letter is the first impression you will make; therefore your presentation must be of a high standard (see below). You should maintain a professional and formal approach throughout the letter and use concise language. The narrative in your letter should enable the reader to gain a positive view of your character and commitment towards pursuing your goal.

### Adhere to letter writing rules:

- Your address should appear on the top **right-hand** corner.
- The employer's address should be on the **left-hand** side, below the level of your address on the right (see example letter below).
- Date the letter on the right-hand side below your address.
- Align addresses and margins; presentation/font should be consistent.
- Your first line under 'Dear Mr X' may be highlighted in bold, stating the application job/course/scholarship reference number.
- Use 'Yours sincerely' prior to signing your name at the end of the letter, if you know the person's name.
- Use 'Yours faithfully' when you are starting your letter with 'Dear Sir/ Madam', i.e. addressing an unnamed person.
- Give an email address and current phone number. Use a current work email if you are qualified or a university email address if you are a student. If near to the end of your university programme, it is acceptable to give a home email address, as your university email will eventually be deactivated.
- Type your formal full name under your signature e.g. Mrs Carol Forde-Johnston.

## Paragraph content for a covering letter

An example structure for paragraphs within your letter is presented below; however, you do not have to prescriptively adhere to these paragraphs. Your narrative can be individualised to your own style, personality and career needs.

**Paragraph 1: Introduction** – brief introduction to summarise your role/career development. Refer to the job advert and/or opportunity offered and give the specific reason for writing the letter. You may wish to convey your enthusiasm for pursuing this particular opportunity to grab their attention early.

**Paragraph 2: Why you chose this organisation/institution and/or opportunity** – state why you have chosen to apply for this specific employer/institution and why you wish to pursue the opportunity with them. State concisely what it means to you personally and how it relates to your role and/or current or future career progression.

**Main body, paragraphs 3/4/5: Summarise why the opportunity is specifically suited to you** – summarise key experiences, skills, competencies, achievements and awards relevant to your application. Focus on the positives about the role/opportunity on offer and how it may impact on your future development or area of interest. Refer to your CV and personal statement for further detail and signpost all related documents. Remember, you cannot include everything in your letter and you should pick out key achievements that link to the role/opportunity. You may also wish to explain an important issue, e.g. if you had to take a year out of university.

**Paragraph 6: Conclusion** – the final sentence should end on a positive thought or request for the future.

## Example covering letter

An example fictitious covering letter from a third year adult nursing student is presented below. This covering letter would be sent alongside a CV with no personal statement, therefore the paragraphs are comprehensive. Always keep a record of past letters and other application documents, as paragraphs can be cut and pasted or reworked for future personal statements in different roles. Also, note how the student has related her voluntary experiences and development to the field of trauma, even though she has not worked on a trauma ward as a student.

Employer's full name, title and address with postcode:
Mrs Kirrane (Trauma Ward Sister)
Oxford University Hospitals NHS Foundation Trust
Headley Way
Headington
OXFORD
OX3 9DU

Your full contact address and postcode
Contact email
Contact telephone number

1st April 2020

Dear Mrs Kirrane,
**Speculative application for a trauma band 5 role** (or state role or course title and reference number)

I am a third year adult nursing student in my final semester at Manchester University, due to qualify as a Registered Nurse in July 2020 with a predicted 2:1 degree. I am writing for your consideration as I wish to apply for my first band 5 staff nurse post in your trauma unit, which is part of the world-renowned Oxford University Hospitals NHS Foundation Trust. I am a hardworking and motivated student who is passionate about developing my career in trauma care. This is demonstrated by my chosen dissertation topic, which is examining how nurses can meet the nutritional needs of trauma patients in UK hospital wards.

In September 2019, I organised an informal visit during the John Radcliffe hospital's recruitment event and was warmly welcomed by your clinical educators, who introduced me to staff across your four trauma wards. During this visit, I was impressed by the level of professional development support and structured preceptorship offered to newly qualified nurses. This inspired me to contact you with a view to developing my future career within your service. As a first year student, I was nominated as student representative for our 2017 nursing cohort. The leadership and communication skills I have developed over the last 3 years in this support role make me an ideal person to join such a collaborative team as yours.

Although I have not experienced a trauma placement during my nursing degree, my interest in trauma care has grown. Experiencing acute care placements within neurosciences and respiratory specialisms increased my understanding of advanced nursing assessment skills across these specialities. As an Air Ambulance volunteer, I observed how the key principles of critical specialist care and team work impacted on patient outcomes. I hope to consolidate what I have already learnt to develop a broader range of acute care knowledge and skills to support trauma inpatients in the future. I aspire to become a clinical educator within trauma, as I have really enjoyed teaching colleagues and patients during my degree. During my course I received the highest marks when assignments were linked to teaching.

I am passionate about person-centred care and treating people with compassion, which aligns with your hospital Trust's core values. During my second year on a ward caring for older people, I completed a poster presentation entitled: 'The impact of loneliness on an older person' that concluded with person-centred strategies to prevent loneliness in older people. My ward mentor encouraged me to present my poster on a nursing assistant study day to highlight the issue of loneliness in society and to promote a group discussion.

My attached CV further details the range of placements I have experienced and the knowledge, skills and competencies I have developed during my degree. I hope you can see the passion I have for pursuing a career in trauma and that you will consider my request for further information relating to potential band 5 posts. I look forward to hearing from you in the future.


Yours sincerely


*(add your signature)*

Mrs Clodagh Forde-Johnston

*Figure 4.1: Example fictitious speculative letter from a third year adult nursing student.*

## 4.3 HOW TO WRITE YOUR PERSONAL STATEMENT

Often individuals struggle most with writing their personal statement, as it consists of free text that is less structured, in comparison to listing factual data in a CV. Some employers and institutions request that you upload a separate personal statement, whereas others ask you to complete a short 'supporting information' or 'additional information' section on an application form. It is helpful to have a personal statement already prepared, as an ongoing active document, so that you can cut and paste key sentences into a 'supporting information' section on an application form.

Whether you write a personal statement, or have to type 150 words of supporting information, you need to demonstrate three key things:

1. Why you want to work for 'them' or want this opportunity, which should align to your career progression
2. That you have the necessary qualities, experience, skills and professional/academic development to meet the demands of the job or opportunity on offer
3. Why they should choose you (you need to 'sell' yourself).

I have not prescriptively defined the content for paragraphs within a personal statement like the covering letter in *Figure 4.1*, as your narrative will flow according to your writing style and professional development. However, a few tips are presented below to guide your personal statement:

- **Establish the word limit:** always stick to the word limit set. The UK Universities and Colleges Admissions Service (UCAS) recommends that a personal statement for a university application is no more than 500 words or 4000 characters. When applying for scholarships, secondments or research funding, a word limit is usually set that may be similar or considerably less.
- **Never add additional data that is not requested:** if you need to detail additional information, then send an email or write a covering letter (see the sample in *Figure 4.1*).
- **Use an essay-type format:** personal statements should be written using an essay-type format that includes an introduction, main paragraphs and a conclusion. You should not present tables and bullets in your personal statement.
- **Review the job description:** it is important to note the key skills within the job description before completing your personal statement. Aim to align practical examples from your current role to themed areas in the job description. You cannot cover every theme and you need to play to your strengths and best practical examples. A band

5 may demonstrate their use of evidence-based practice from a care plan they updated that was informed by new NICE guidelines and national standards. In contrast, a band 6 may have conducted a pilot evaluation to inform local practice. Although there will be different distinctions between bands, most job descriptions will include a variety of skills relating to key themes, such as:
- organisation of care, leadership and management
- communication
- teamworking
- safe care, standard-setting and adhering to policy
- use of EBP
- flexibility and ability to adapt to new situations
- ability to work well under pressure and manage stress
- desire to develop and progress
- ability to work independently, autonomously and to be self-directed.
- **Focus on your 'best' examples:** do not detail every aspect of your career to date when writing a personal statement. Choose your **best examples** and **most relevant achievements** that relate to what you are applying for. Ideally one project or achievement may demonstrate several skills required (see example projects in *Section 3.2.1*).
- **Don't forget to detail 'the impact':** it is great having practical examples of your achievements within your personal statement but **'so what?'** Always detail the impact your examples have had on others, or on a service. You cannot provide the same level of detail as a dissertation; however, just a few specific evaluative comments can raise a personal statement from fair or good to outstanding.

*Example 1*, below, describes an interesting project led by a band 5 working in theatres, but there is a lack of specifics. This contrasts with *Example 2*, which clearly details the impact of the project on their theatre service. *Example 2* also begins by aligning one of the key personal specifications in the job description: 'promoting positive team work' and ends with future dissemination to others.

### Example 1

During the last 3 months I have been leading a pilot project in spinal theatres with the support of the 'PatientSafe Network'. The aim of this pilot is to introduce and evaluate named theatre caps, which has been positively received by our staff.

**Example 2**

My passion for promoting positive team working has been demonstrated during the last 6 months, whilst leading a pilot project in spinal theatres with the support of the national 'PatientSafe Network'. The aim of the pilot was to introduce named theatre caps over a 6-month period and evaluate whether they improved staff communications. Feedback from a questionnaire sent to 40 new starter staff indicated that 90% did not feel able to approach their theatre colleagues for help during their first 6 months in post. The main reasons given were a lack of awareness of who staff were and what their role was. This project reflects national drivers from the #TheatreCapChallenge, PatientSafe Network and Chris Pointon/Kate Granger's #hellomynameis campaign, which aim to increase theatre staff engagement through knowing staff names/roles and to prevent adverse events relating to communication errors. Our pilot team is currently evaluating the impact of named theatre caps on staff morale and the increased propensity of staff to speak up. We aim to publish and disseminate the results of our project in a national journal and at the National Patient Safety Conference next year.

### 4.3.1 Example personal statements

Two fictitious 500-word personal statements are presented below. *Example A* is from a third year adult nursing student applying for their first post in the community. Note how this statement is distinct from the student's particular career path and they have aligned their experiences and developing knowledge and skills to the community role. The narrative in *Example A* is personable, and well thought out, and it flows. The student is at an advantage following an informal visit, as they are able to relate positively to the team with conviction. There is evidence of compassion; a person-centred approach; positive teamworking; evidence-based practice; critical research skills; self-directed learning; safe and effective care; motivation to develop in the future; and organisation and leadership. *Example A*'s narrative focuses more on patient-centred care that might contrast with a personal statement for ICU, which could draw out more advanced critical and specialist skill development.

*Example B*'s personal statement is from an experienced band 5 RM applying to their current manager for academic funding and study leave. Within the narrative there is evidence of initiative; motivation and ambition; the capacity to practically apply knowledge and self-direct learning; active involvement in supporting others; research activity; and a clear understanding of how the course will contribute to their development. All these factors demonstrate the level of commitment a manager would wish to see, prior to funding an individual's course fees/study days. You can clearly see how practical examples and projects in the band 5's current role have been integrated to demonstrate their commitment.

### *Example A* Personal statement for a third year student applying for a community post

I am a third year adult nursing student in my final semester at university, currently predicted to receive a 2:2 degree. I am a kind, hardworking and motivated person who is committed to providing person-centred care to support individuals at home, hence my application for a band 5 community staff nurse role. Having completed mostly ward placements and an 18-week community placement, I realise that I prefer care in the community to support people in their own homes, in comparison to working across contained hospital environments.

During an informal visit to your Community Health Trust, I met supportive clinical educators who discussed your preceptorship programme. I have been inspired to apply to your Trust, as your team recognises the need for practical education and skill development to enable staff to thrive on qualification. I understand the importance of positive team working to promote positive patient outcomes. I feel that my encouraging nature fits well with the ethos of your collaborative interdisciplinary team. I am relocating back to this area with my partner and my long-term goal is to progress along a career pathway within a local team to become a community specialist nurse in learning disabilities.

In 2015, I volunteered for our local Down's Syndrome Association in a role supporting community activities. Working with young people nurtured my interest in caring for others in the community and inspired me to start my adult nursing degree. My voluntary work has continued throughout my degree and I have learnt the importance of using a holistic approach to ensure individuals are not labelled with a disability. My goal in nursing is to enable individuals' decision-making using a person-centred approach to promote future independence, which aligns to your community Trust's core values. This area of interest has been further developed in my dissertation, which is a literature review examining existing evidence-based person-centred community (PCC) models for older adults. Completing this review has developed my critical research skills and increased my insight of PCC models for use in home and community-based services. My goal is to utilise strategies from my review and evaluate their use in the future, along with completing a master's to examine how organisational factors may influence the delivery of person-centred community services.

The acute and long-term placements I have experienced during my degree, detailed in my application form, have enabled me to become a safe and effective practitioner. Whilst working on a busy neurosurgical ward during my final year, I consolidated key organisational and leadership skills to competently care for a caseload of 6 patients. Whilst caring for adults who were neurologically compromised, I provided wound care for confused individuals and supported adults who requested to self-discharge or decline care. These complex experiences increased my knowledge and competence while adhering to national/local policies, guidelines and standards. Key areas covered, such as critical and specialist care assessment and observation; escalation; mental capacity assessment; Deprivation of Liberty Safeguards and risk assessments will enhance and inform my care as a future community nurse.

### *Example B* Personal statement for an experienced RM applying for course funding

In September 2017, I commenced our local midwifery rotational preceptorship programme as a newly registered midwife. The 18-month structured rotation took place across our antenatal and postnatal ward, high risk labour ward and community setting. Following rotations, I realised that my future career lay within our high risk labour unit. In July 2019, I was appointed as a band 5 within this service, which includes: high risk labour wards; bereavement suite; recovery; induction of labour; and High Dependency Unit.

I am a caring, enthusiastic person who is committed to supporting staff and parents across our services. I have always had a specialist interest in the support of parents after stillbirth. As a 3rd year student, I chose to conduct a systematic literature review examining bereaved parents' experience of stillbirth in UK hospitals. Recommendations included the need for midwives to be educated in bereavement support and ward environments to be more conducive to supporting bereaved parents. My interest in this field has grown and I offered to become the bereavement link midwife for my area last year. As part of this role, I organised 10 cake sales to generate funds to decorate our bereavement room; self-funded a Royal College of Midwives conference on bereavement; joined the Bereavement Care Network to share best practice; and taught on the preceptorship programme to support newly qualified midwives. My ultimate goal is to become an Advanced Midwifery Practitioner in Bereavement, to support staff and patients affected by miscarriage, stillbirth or loss of a baby after birth.

As an experienced band 5, I actively support our clinical educators by leading monthly walk-rounds to orientate midwifery students. Walk-rounds take place two weeks before placement starts and many students have commented on how unusual it is to be offered an additional pre-placement visit and how my encouragement decreased their nerves. Last month I received a commendation from the University for my support of students and was awarded 'Best practice supervisor' following student nominations.

The areas of research that inspire me most are those linked to parent experiences and bereavement support. This led to recent research collaboration with a local university team who were tasked with completing an evaluative audit across our hospitals to improve ward environments. Audit findings helped to inform the refurbishment of our bereavement suite, which included introducing new soundproofing so parents/other family members did not have to pass expectant or new parents and babies. Being part of this project increased my understanding of how research can positively influence practice and led me to apply to commence my MSc in Advanced Practice (Midwifery) at Oxford Brookes University. During my MSc I aspire to advance my research skills to further examine parents' experiences of care after bereavement.

I hope you can see the passion I have for positively influencing future care within our unit and that you will consider my request for support with MSc fees and study leave. The cost of modules and number of study days required are detailed in my covering letter.

## 4.4 CURRICULUM VITAE (CV) TEMPLATE

The Latin term curriculum vitae (CV) is loosely translated as meaning 'the course of my life'. A CV may be used when applying speculatively for a future role/opportunity that is not currently being advertised, or as part of a current application to help the shortlisting process. A classically constructed CV consists of a short written description, usually only two pages long, which provides an overview of the following:

- **Name:** your name centred at the top of the CV should stand out using larger or bold text. Do not have the words Curriculum Vitae at the top of your CV.
- **Contact information:** ensure contact details for your email and telephone number are current. If you are nearing the end of university, then provide a home address and personal email, as your university account will terminate on completion of your course. Never include your address or date of birth on a CV, as personal data can be stolen.
- **Personal profile or career summary:** a personal profile or career summary is a punchy focused statement (just a few sentences in one paragraph), that aims to capture the reader's attention. It is written in a style similar to that used in an advert in a newspaper. This is why it is found at the top of your CV under the contact information, to set the scene. A personal profile statement should cover three areas:
  1. Who you are
  2. What your skills are
  3. What you want.

An example personal profile for a final year mental health student is presented below:

"Highly motivated, diligent and hardworking third year mental health nursing student, received excellent feedback on every placement and predicted to receive 2:1 degree classification. Compassionate and patient-focused approach to care, promotes positive communication to thrive when collaborating within a team environment. Seeks a band 5 inpatient mental health nurse role to consolidate skills from degree and develop career to become a senior mental health practitioner."

A personal profile statement is **optional** on a CV and you do not need to force one out if it does not flow naturally.

- **Education:** present your most recent qualifications and courses first then work backwards. List the institution (full name); degree studied (full name); grade/award/classification; start date and date achieved. Always use separate headings to split general education (school) from professional education (degree/post-registration).

  You can summarise early school qualifications on one line to save space:

  A Levels: Geography (C); English (A)..., etc.

  GCSEs: A* grades in English, Maths and Chemistry, B grades in Biology..., etc.

  A table may help to detail your qualifications; see below:

| Institution | Title of course | Award/grade | Start date & date achieved |
|---|---|---|---|
| University of Manchester | BSc (Hons) in Mental Health Nursing | 2:1 | Sept 2016–July 2019 |

- **Employment history and professional skills developed:** similar to the education section above, always start with the most recent employment first and work backwards. You should present your employment start date and end date (month/year); the title of the role; the employer's full name and location; and description of main duties/skills developed. Some CVs separate the employment history and skills into a table with key headings, whereas others use bullet points to list skills below an employer heading. You can use whichever format fits best with your narrative content.

Use action verbs and adjectives to demonstrate the key skills and learning achieved on your CV. Students may wish to differentiate between placements within their skills section; see an example below that uses a bullet style of presentation:

January 2019–July 2019
Final 3rd year placement on an acute neurosurgical ward:
- Assessed neurologically deteriorating individuals using the Glasgow Coma Scale.
- Competently escalated deteriorating individuals to medics adhering to the Trust escalation policy and National Early Warning Scores (NEWS2)
- Effectively organised and managed a caseload of 6 patients by delegating to nursing assistants and first year students.
- Accurately documented key risk assessments required for adult inpatients and provided key strategies to prevent risks following assessment.

- **Awards/achievements:** highlight any awards or achievements you have received, e.g. a high classification for a degree/post-registration course; student/staff recognition award; acting as student/staff representative; poster presentation used in clinical practice; collaborating with a national network; managing to complete a course through adversity; publications and presenting at conferences. You may add any social/community-based achievements outside nursing too.
- **Interests:** you may wish to state a few current interests; however, do not add interests for the sake of it.
- **References:** present the contact details of two referees at the end of your CV (see *References, Section 4.2*).

### 4.4.1 Additional guidance

Further guidance is presented below, reflecting some of the questions I am asked by staff and students about their CV.

### What template should I use?

If you type 'CV templates' into an online search engine you will find over a million examples. If it is your first time writing a CV, RCN members can use the helpful RCN website resource *CV Writing for Student Nurses and Newly Qualified Nurses* (RCN, 2019b). This service allows you to construct your own CV and the RCN will provide feedback on your CV once completed, via email at career.service@rcn.org.uk.

### Does it matter what order I present my qualifications and employment in?

Yes. You should present your qualifications and employment in reverse chronological order on a CV, which means putting your **most recent first**. This chronological order is widely accepted in healthcare and university fields, as it is the most helpful sequence to a busy recruiter who needs to review many applications.

### Can I put pictures and photos on my CV?

No. Healthcare CVs should not include pictures or photos and they should be simply and professionally presented using narrative only. Your CV should maintain an excellent standard of presentation (see *Presentation matters*, *Section 4.2*). With the advent of social media and increasing use of visual technology, I suspect that the traditional tabular CV will eventually evolve to include visual format such as video uploads. Alternative CV formats may help individuals with dyslexia or visual learners; however, we are not there yet and traditional CV formats are still currently expected.

### Should I write a new CV each time?

There is no need to redo your CV completely each time. Remember a CV is an 'active' document that you can revisit and adjust to align with different audiences. However, always make sure you **check which CV you are sending to whom**. Over the years I have been sent CVs aimed at different employers or roles, clearly by mistake. It is very easy to make this error when storing data using computer folders; we are all human.

 **KEY TIP**

- Always check your attached CV before you press Send.

### What happens if I lie on my CV?

Never embellish information on your CV. In cases where a qualification is legally required to carry out a job, such as NMC registration, legal action could be taken against you if you falsify data. If you have career gaps, it is better to be honest and justify them through a covering letter or during your interview.

## 4.5 PERSONAL PROFESSIONAL PORTFOLIO

### 4.5.1 What is a personal professional portfolio?

Following registration, healthcare professionals should create a professional portfolio that provides a bespoke overview of evidence relating to their career development and practice experiences to date. Your portfolio may be paper-based or an electronic e-portfolio and there are excellent example templates relating to both provided by the RCN (2019c) and NMC (2019).

### 4.5.2 What is it used for?

Your professional portfolio may provide evidence to support the following:
- Future Professional Development Reviews.
- Three-yearly revalidation review (see *Section 2.6* on NMC registration and revalidation).
- Applications and interviews for future jobs, educational funding, secondments or scholarships.

### 4.5.3 Can I present my personal portfolio using visual or audio methods?

Yes. Personal professional portfolios are a reflection of 'you' and evidence may be creatively presented using visual or audio methods, if you prefer. I am reviewing more and more portfolios that are imaginatively presented using video, audio files, links to personal blogs or alternative electronic formats.

### 4.5.4 How do I present the sections within my portfolio?

You should always present evidence clearly, using defined sections to demonstrate good organisation. However, you may design your own portfolio structure to suit the content when you are dividing sections. I have read portfolios starting with a patient thank you card, or a quote from a practice supervisor that introduces the person as a 'compassionate practitioner'. Others may start with a current job description, personal statement or CV. Structuring your portfolio really depends on your style and preferences and how content relates best to each section.

Start collecting evidence for your professional portfolio during your first few months qualified. Once your portfolio is structured, you can keep updating the evidence as your career progresses and you attend study days. Your portfolio will usually contain headed sections such as the ones presented below:
- **Title and contents:** signpost your content using a contents page or a list of defined sections/headings. Paper-based portfolios can be placed in a folder using plastic wallets and dividing tabs. E-portfolio templates are already structured and you just need to upload evidence, e.g. electronic certificates of eLearning packages or study days.
- **Introduction:** should explain the purpose of the portfolio, your current role and an overview of the structure and sections used.
- **Personal statement:** see *Section 4.3*.
- **Current job description:** a copy of your current job description and/ or summary of current responsibilities. International nurses working

in the UK find this particularly helpful to explain a band 5/6/7 role if they return home, as career structures and responsibilities can differ between countries.

- **CV:** see *Section 4.4.*
- **CPD:** see examples in *Table 2.4.*
- **Practice-related feedback:** see examples in *Table 2.4.*
- **Reflective accounts:** see examples in *Table 2.4.*
- **Achievements:** examples for this section may include:
  - Summary/abstract of local service improvement project or research
  - PowerPoint from a teaching session
  - Awards, scholarships or research bursaries
  - Photos/narrative from recent events you have supported
  - Charity work/projects or interests that demonstrate transferable skills
  - Publications – you may present full article if published in a national journal.

Include brief notes/reflections to explain how your achievements have influenced your practice.

--- **WHAT TO DO NEXT** ---

1. Rigorously check the shortlisting criteria for roles/courses in advance, to ensure that you have the qualifications/experience required to be shortlisted. Minimum 'essential' requirements for a job or academic course will be detailed in the job personal specification or course entry criteria.
2. Align as many 'desirable' personal specification requirements as you can in advance, to strengthen future applications and demonstrate your suitability for a role/course on offer.
3. Review a variety of CV and professional portfolio templates online, e.g. templates provided by the RCN (2019b) and NMC (2019).
4. Spend time and effort producing a professional CV, personal statement and professional portfolio that can be used as a 'live' document and updated at short notice when needed.
5. Write concise narrative that clearly demonstrates you have the necessary qualities, experience, skills and professional/academic qualifications to meet the demands of the job/course on offer. Present your best case examples and most relevant achievements that relate to what you are applying for. Detail the impact your examples have had on a service or others.

6. Thoroughly review guidance notes prior to completing an application form and follow instructions to the letter, e.g. adhere to the closing date deadline. Spend time and effort completing application forms and review your application several times for any mistakes prior to uploading or posting documents.

## REFERENCES AND FURTHER READING

Equality Act (2010). Available at: www.legislation.gov.uk/ukpga/2010/15/contents [accessed 11 December 2019]

Greaves, I. (2019) *Disability Rights Handbook, edition 44: April 2019– April 2020.* Disability Rights UK.

Mawhinney, G., Thakar, C., Williamson, V. *et al.* (2019) Oxford Video Informed Consent Tool (OxVIC): a pilot study of informed video consent in spinal surgery and preoperative patient satisfaction. *BMJ Open* 2019; **9**:e027712. Available at: https://bmjopen.bmj.com/content/9/7/e027712 [accessed 11 December 2019]

Nursing and Midwifery Council (2019) *Revalidation/Resources: forms and templates.* NMC. Available at: http://revalidation.nmc.org.uk/download-resources/forms-and-templates.html [accessed 11 December 2019]

Oppenheimer, D.M. (2006) Consequences of erudite vernacular utilized irrespective of necessity: problems with using long words needlessly. *Applied Cognitive Psychology,* **20**(2): 139–156.

Royal College of Nursing (2019a) *RCN Careers Resources.* RCN. Available at: www.rcn.org.uk/professional-development/your-career [accessed 11 December 2019]

Royal College of Nursing (2019b) *CV Writing for Student Nurses and Newly Qualified Nurses.* RCN. Available at: www.rcn.org.uk/professional-development/your-career/student/student-nurse-cv-writing [accessed 11 December 2019]

Royal College of Nursing (2019c) *Revalidation.* RCN. Available at: www.rcn.org.uk/professional-development/revalidation [accessed 11 December 2019]

Royal College of Physicians (2017) *National Early Warning Score (NEWS2): standardising the assessment of acute-illness severity in the NHS.* RCP. Available at: www.rcplondon.ac.uk/projects/outputs/national-early-warning-score-news-2 [accessed 11 December 2019]

Equality Act (2010) Available at: www.legislation.gov.uk/ukpga/2010/15/contents [accessed 11 December 2019]

# STEP 5

# CREATE AN INTERVIEW PLAN

*"We should remember that good fortune often happens
when opportunity meets with preparation."*
Thomas Edison (1847–1931), inventor of the light bulb

## 5.1 THE MORE YOU PREPARE, THE BETTER CHANCE YOU HAVE OF SUCCEEDING

Previous steps within this book support Thomas Edison's view that *'good fortune'*, such as positive career advancement, is more likely to happen *'when opportunity meets preparation'*. *Steps 1* and *2* highlight the importance of aligning your professional and academic development with a career pathway. *Step 3* supports implementing projects to make your CV and personal statement stand out, and *Step 4* offers guidance on completing a strong application. This chapter focuses on creating an interview plan to help you perform to the best of your ability during an interview.

I have spent many years advising third year students and registered/ non-registered staff, offering to review their application documents, provide mock interviews, or give support after the interview if they were unsuccessful. Those who were not appointed either did not spend enough time preparing responses to interview questions, or another applicant simply interviewed better than them on the day.

### 5.1.1 Allocate time to prepare

Once an interview has been secured, you should spend sufficient time preparing answers to potential questions and practising your responses. Allocate a day or more to preparation time, as opposed to a few hours. It is important to prepare mentally and physically before an interview, which includes planning logistics to arrive on time, organising the documentation required, and calming your nerves.

Remember, when applying for highly sought-after clinical settings, band 6 or 7 posts, secondment development opportunities, and places on professional/academic courses, another opportunity may not arise for a while. It is important to block out interview preparation time in your diary; then you will always know that you gave the interview your best shot, whatever the outcome.

### 5.1.2 The importance of preparing questions and practising responses

When undertaking any competition, you rarely do well without regular practice, and the same goes for interviews. Preparing answers to potential questions and undertaking mock interviews are rehearsals for the interview day, which increase your chance of success. Someone who is nervous, but able to concisely apply practical examples and a passion for a role or service, will have more chance of succeeding than someone who is confident in presenting themselves but is ill-prepared and offers little substance in their answers.

Many employers use value-based recruitment (VBR) techniques that rigorously review and rate interviewees' answers. It is much easier for interviewers to compare candidates who have carefully prepared, with those who have not. Candidates need to concisely integrate relevant clinical examples within their responses to meet the criteria being measured and increase their rating scores (see *Section 5.2.2*).

### 5.1.3 Never presume a role or opportunity is yours

Presuming that a role or opportunity is yours is a fatal mistake that is sometimes made by experienced staff who feel that they are 'next in line', or by individuals who have been encouraged to apply by colleagues. They develop a false sense of security and make little effort to prepare for their interview. Although interviewers take account of individuals' past experiences and achievements, it is important to remember that any staff member shortlisted has the potential to succeed, which includes the most recent person to join your team (see *Section 4.2.1*).

### 5.1.4 Differentiating between candidates who all perform well

When several interviewees have performed to a similar high standard, interviewers will rigorously review their application documents. Aligning your professional and academic development to a career pathway will inevitably increase your chance of progression. The more competitive the role or opportunities on offer, the better prepared your application, CV and/or personal statement should be (see *Step 4* for example application templates).

Interview preparation should never be neglected and the following section presents practical guidance to structure an interview plan that includes: an overview of different types of interviews, so you know what to expect; background preparation to formulate potential interview questions and responses; and guidance to help organisation on the actual day. A summary of what happens after your interview, how to deal with multiple job offers and how to learn from interview feedback is also presented.

## 5.2 DIFFERENT TYPES OF INTERVIEWS

During your career you may be invited to different types of interviews that encompass a variety of formats, such as:
- face-to-face, in person
- telephone or Skype
- group interview
- competency assessments
- informal preliminary.

An overview of each type of interview is presented below, including what to expect and practical tips to inform your preparation.

### 5.2.1 Always check the type of interview being employed

It is important to check which type of interview you will be undertaking so you know exactly what to expect on the day and you can prepare accordingly. You may have to deal with a mixture of arrangements; for example, a pre-prepared 15-minute presentation may be required for a band 6/7 post, followed by face-to-face questioning from an interview panel that includes medics and AHPs.

An interview invitation will be sent by letter/email and it should clearly state what type of arrangements will be in place on the day, along with associated timings. Some competency-based simulation assessments may require your attendance all day in an assessment centre. If in doubt, you can request further information from the recruitment lead. It is rare that band 5 interviews are complex; however, as you rise up a career ladder, the interview criteria and assessments inevitably become more challenging.

## Face-to-face, in person

What to expect
- A standard and traditional type of interview.
- Interviewing may take place 1:1 or in front of an interview panel.
- Interview conducted in a closed interview room for confidentiality.
- Interviewee asked a series of questions from each interviewer.
- A lead interviewer chairs the interview and manages time.
- To reduce bias, interviews usually involve two or more interviewers.
- Usually last 30 minutes for band 5 roles and may last 45–60 minutes for a senior position.
- One of the interviewers will continually take notes in a values-based interview (see *Section 5.2.2*).

Practical tips
- Collate and analyse background information relating to the opportunity (see *Section 5.3.1*).
- Prepare potential questions and responses (see *Table 5.1*).
- Arrange a mock interview with a senior colleague who is not on the interview panel (see *Section 5.2.3*).
- Ask a senior person for interview advice, such as a university lecturer, mentor, clinical supervisor, team leader or a person currently in the role.
- Aim to arrive for your interview an hour beforehand, to allow time to deal with any unexpected delays and to compose yourself.
- During the interview use open body posture and language (see *Section 5.4*) and dress smartly (see *Section 5.4.4*).

## Telephone or Skype

What to expect
- Media are used for a teleconferencing interview, such as a telephone or video conferencing systems.
- Regularly used for international recruitment or when UK candidates are unable to travel.
- Prior to Skype interview, you will be sent a Skype link to connect with the lead interviewer/organisation.
- Questions presented to candidates will be the same as face-to-face interviews and, similarly, interviewers will write notes as the candidate speaks.

Practical tips
- Prior to appointment, overseas applicants must demonstrate proficiency in English, attaining International English Language Testing System (IELTS) level 7.0 or equivalent Oxford English Test (OET).
- Preparing questions for Skype and telephone interviews should be as rigorous as face-to-face interviews.
- Telephone interviews allow you to have notes out in front of you and you can wear your pyjamas if you want, as no one can see you!
- Responding well to questions, whilst using an engaging tone, is important during telephone/Skype interviews. Aim to sound approachable, whilst being professionally competent.
- Skype/telephone interviews rely on technology working, so always test out connections before the interview day.
- Choose an appropriate venue, such as a closed study/office to prevent disturbances. Make sure the venue is tidy and organised for Skype interviews.
- Print out interview details and relevant contacts/names in case of connection issues on the day.
- During the interview turn phones off and take animals/children out of the room (see *Children Interrupt BBC News Interview* for an example of what can go wrong! (BBC News, 2017)).

## Group

What to expect
- Involves a group working together on a set task, either in one big group or smaller subsets.
- The interviewer explains task and/or instructions are written down, either on a handout or screen.
- Group tasks may include: discussing a current topic; analysing an ethical dilemma; solving a problem or role-playing a scenario.
- Each member of the group is observed and notes are written about each person's performance and behaviours.
- Criteria are set to measure and rate each individual's performance, e.g. demonstrates organisational and leadership skills; an ability to work with others; uses a team approach and shows respect towards peers.
- Group work usually lasts longer than standard face-to-face interviews and sometimes candidates rotate across a series of different tasks over a day.

Practical tips
- Read instructions thoroughly; if it states: *'summarise your thoughts on a flip chart'* then do this and encourage group members to complete the task.
- If one person dominates the group, leading others down the wrong path, do not be afraid to respectfully point out the instructions.
- If you do not agree with someone, respectfully challenge, by presenting an alternative perspective in a constructive manner.
- Recruiters assess candidates' strengths/weaknesses and will look out for lack of self-awareness; talking over others; not listening or respecting alternative views, and unprofessionalism.
- Always contribute to group work and start by introducing yourself.
- Do not view group members as competitors, as the aim is to work together as a team.
- Remember, your interview starts when you walk in the door of an institution. All observed behaviour is assessed, including during breaks and before/after group work. Do not be drawn into messing around and being seen as not taking tasks seriously.
- Switch your mobile phone off so you are not tempted to use it during the day.

## Competency assessments

What to expect
- A variety of assessments, tests and tools can be used during interviews to assess the competency and proficiency levels of a candidate, such as:
  - narrative based questions using scenario/cases
  - scenario-based role play
  - pre-prepared presentation
  - simulation
  - numeracy, psychometric or aptitude test.
- Band 5 roles do not usually require additional competency assessments. Posts from band 6 upwards may use a range of competency-based techniques.
- You usually have no prior warning before the interview of questions or the type of tests you will be undertaking.
- Question papers/tests will be under exam conditions to ensure no cheating takes place.
- If required to deliver a presentation, the topic will be given to you prior to your interview.
- The resources available for presentations are usually stated on your invitation.

## Practical tips

### *Case study questions and scenarios*

- Under exam conditions you cannot usually ask the examiner to clarify the question. Increase your awareness of key terminology to ensure you understand any question(s) posed (see *Step 3, Tables 3.2–3.5*).
- Use a methodical approach when answering questions, such as the Nursing Process: Assess, Plan, Implement and Evaluate (APIE) (Orlando, 1961), or ABCDE (Resuscitation Council, 2015).
- Competency-based assessments often relate to a communication or safety issue that requires de-escalation or escalation. Review current evidence bases and national policies/guidelines relating to escalation/incident reporting.
- Prepare for specialist case scenarios (see *Section 5.3.1* and *Table 5.1*).
- Documentation skills will be reviewed within narrative-based questions. Adhere to national NMC standards of record-keeping, which are covered by the *Code* (NMC, 2018a), and ensure that:
  - your documentation is legible and clear
  - the meaning is correct, accurate and professional
  - your writing style is concise and factual; and not ambiguous, emotive or judgemental.

### *Simulation*

- Most healthcare students/staff have undertaken simulated exercises at some time, such as role play; an Objective Structured Clinical Examination (OSCE); Basic Life Support or Recognising the Acutely Ill and Deteriorating Patient (RAID) assessments. Reflect on your weaknesses and strengths to inform your preparation.
- Recruiters look for a competent and methodical approach, e.g. systematic use of ABCDE (Resuscitation Council UK, 2015).
- If concerned about your performance, ask colleagues/local educators to provide mock simulations.
- Never forget to introduce yourself to a patient during a simulation and maintain a compassionate and professional approach throughout.

### *Presentation*

- Never take shortcuts when preparing a presentation, as your performance may be the difference between being appointed or not. Always keep to the brief and check key terms/definitions to be sure.

- Interview presentations are usually 10–20 minutes. Keep to time, as you may be asked to stop. If you have a tendency to overrun, rehearse timings.
- Review the related evidence base and integrate key references into your presentation. The key is providing an engaging talk, underpinned by personal experience and references.
- Structure your presentation into an introduction, main body and conclusion:
  - introduction – overview of what will be covered and/or aim/ objectives (may be verbal if short of time)
  - main body – background experiences/literature followed by main points that answer the question, always informed by current evidence base
  - conclusion – leave your audience with a positive message, quote, photo or personal perspective.
- Most candidates provide straightforward PowerPoint slides, although other presentation methods may be used, such as a poster. Never risk using a new strategy unless well-rehearsed.
- Ensure slides are of an excellent quality and visually appealing, with no mistakes.
- It is fine to use cue cards but do not look down the whole time. Look up, smile and make eye contact with the audience at various points throughout the presentation. You may put a star in places on your notes to remind you, in case you forget due to nerves.
- Colleagues may be asked to attend presentations, especially for band 7/8 posts. Plan for questions and never use words that you do not fully understand.
- Provide a hard copy of the presentation for each interviewer and include a reference list.

### Numeracy, psychometric and aptitude tests
- Numeracy testing focuses on clinical calculations/reasoning and there are excellent books available to help you prepare, such as Davison (2020), Lapham (2015) and Starkings and Krause (2018). You will be told whether you are allowed a calculator in the test.
- Psychometric and aptitude tests screen for values/personality types. You should answer the questions honestly without trying to second-guess what interviewers are looking for.

## Informal preliminary

### What to expect

- A popular approach used by employers to recruit when there are large numbers of vacant posts. Involves an informal interview that may take place during recruitment fairs or an informal visit.
- Recruiters take you to a quiet spot or may have an interview room booked.
- The aim is to informally question an individual to establish whether a role suits a person's skills and whether they fit into a team.
- No formal job offer will be agreed until your application documentation is received and references/occupational health checks are completed.

### Practical tips

- Recruiters may verbally offer an 'on the spot' preliminary interview if you approach them with a keen interest. Recruiters take account of nerves and that you have not prepared. If it is a post you are interested in then your passion will shine through!
- Preliminary interviews are less formal than standard interviews; however, you still need to answer questions to the best of your ability and maintain your professionalism throughout.
- You may decline a preliminary interview but remember recruiters offer these interviews when they see potential in you. If you decline, you risk missing out on a post.
- Make sure you have the correct job application link for the correct job, prior to leaving an event. It is helpful to have the lead recruiter's contact details in case of problems later.

## 5.2.2 *What are values-based interviews?*

The aim of values-based interviews (VBIs) is to select individuals who most closely align with the values of an organisation. The interview starts with generic questions, followed by further probing and 'drilling down', according to the individual's responses. An NHS Trust may be 'committed to delivering compassionate care'; therefore, each candidate is asked the same non-specific question: "*Can you define compassionate care for us?*" or "*Give me a recent example where you delivered compassionate care at work.*"

Interviewers will expect a relevant example that demonstrates understanding of the question and practical application. If, after further probing, no specific example is found, i.e. you talk generally about the topic area or reel off a definition with no case example, your answer will be rated low. Interviewees who explicitly demonstrate core skills using practical examples will score much higher in VBIs than those who present broad answers alluding to skills.

### Rating responses according to your answers

During a VBI one person will continuously take notes to record your answers. At the end of the interview all candidates' responses will be analysed using specific rating criteria to establish who should be appointed.

Most employers have a standard interview record form to complete for each candidate to ensure parity across interviews. These forms use rating scales to provide feedback on each answer and the sum of these will lead to a total score. A '0' score would be given if you offer an incorrect or poor answer with no tangible evidence, or a hypothetical answer with no substance. In contrast, a highly rated answer may receive a score of '3', indicating that your responses exceeded all criteria being measured, or the question was positively answered with excellent case examples.

### Focus on your contribution when presenting examples

When presenting examples at interview, you need to give concise background information to place them in context. It is important to focus on what you did and what your role was in relation to the example, not just what a doctor/AHP did. Remember, you are rated on evidence of your skills and contribution, not just your description as a bystander.

Most VBIs examine your contribution in the following key areas, whatever the banding on offer:
• A compassionate and person-centred approach
• Good communication relating to therapeutic relations and/or team working
• Professionalism and safe practice adhering to policy
• Promotion of quality standards through management and leadership
• Ability to cope with challenges and manage stress.

It is helpful to have a good case example prepared demonstrating each of the above areas.

### 5.2.3 Arrange a mock interview

One of the best ways to prepare for an interview, especially if you are nervous or there are several high calibre applicants, is to arrange a mock interview. It is through practice and constructive feedback that we develop as practitioners. I have offered mock interviews to staff who were repeatedly interviewed for band 6/7 posts, without success. Only through constructive feedback from a mock interview were they able to realise that their previous responses were not in sufficient depth. Constructive feedback informed their future answers and enabled them to eventually move up a band.

Requesting a mock interview is perfectly acceptable, as long as the person providing the interview is not on the interview panel. Further tips relating to mock interviews are presented below:

### Who do I ask to do a mock interview?

Ask a supportive experienced colleague, manager or educator. The person should be a respected professional and good role model who can offer sound and constructive advice. If you are a third year student you may ask a personal tutor, academic advisor or senior mentor.

If no professional is free, ask a family member or trusted friend to read out interview questions and rehearse your answers. They can generally give feedback on your performance and you will gain some insights, e.g. your weakest answer to focus more research.

### How do I request a mock interview?

Book a mock interview well in advance of any interview. Requesting a mock interview is totally self-directed, as no one is obliged to offer you one. Offering feedback on your performance will be additional to a person's current workload and should not be expected. However, many supportive managers/educators are happy to oblige, as long as they have the time.

### Will a mock interview make me feel more nervous?

There is no doubt that mock interviews will take you out of your comfort zone and they are not for everyone. A mock interview may be disjointed and awkward; however, it is a brilliant way to inform further preparation and to reassure you about your strengths. So what if you stumble over certain answers? Surely it is better to get the awkwardness out of the way before your actual interview.

## 5.3 CREATE AN INTERVIEW PLAN

It is important to methodically prepare for an interview and any competency-based assessments that are part of a selection process. Creating and implementing an interview plan will involve the following four elements:

1. Completing background work and research
2. Structuring potential questions and responses
3. Practising your answers
4. Preparing physically and psychologically.

### 5.3.1 *The importance of background research*

Prior to structuring responses to potential interview questions, it is important to conduct background research that covers the following key areas:

- Type of interview (see *Section 5.2*)
- Job description, person specification and advert
- The service, role or course/scholarship
- Key healthcare terms and definitions
- Local and national standards
- Current 'hot' topics.

Practical tips relating to these key areas are presented below to guide your research:

### Job description and person specification

- Review the job description, person specification and advert for key words and themes linked to the role, such as 'person-centred approach', 'team working' or 'transformational leadership'. You may be asked about these topics in your interview; therefore, review papers and the current evidence base surrounding these areas. A third year pre-registration student can look back on previous modules and lecture notes to help their revision.
- Similarly, if you are applying for a course, scholarship or secondment, review advertising material and guidance notes. Identify course aims and learning outcomes from university handbooks to inform questions such as: "*Why have you chosen to apply for this course/scholarship?*" or "*Do you know what the course entails?*"

## The service, role or course

Employers expect you to have a sound understanding of the service/role you are applying for. Some example questions are presented below to guide your preparation:
- What is the employer's mission statement and/or what core values do they promote?
- What types of patients and conditions will you come across?
- Is this an established service/role or newly created?
- Are there changes planned? If so, what will this mean to the future service?
- Are there national or local guidelines/standards that influence current services?
- What type of nursing/midwifery systems will you be using?
- Do they use electronic patient records or other e-systems?

If you are applying for a scholarship or bursary you may be questioned on details about the institution, awarding body and/or scholarship being offered (see the overview of national institutions in *Section 3.3*).

The best way to find out about a service or role is to arrange an informal visit to meet senior nurses and educators in the clinical area (see informal visits in *Section 1.2.6*).

## Key healthcare terms and definitions

Every year I interview staff who have no idea what a key healthcare term means, even though they have highlighted it across their personal statements. Increase your understanding of key healthcare terminology to ensure you understand questions relating to:
- teaching and supervision
- evidence-based practice and research
- improving quality and standards
- management and leadership (see *Section 3.4*, *Tables 3.2–3.5*).

## Local/national standards and evidence-based practices

- Review professional standards/proficiencies that link to professional accountability and responsibility.
- Identify evidence-based practices that underpin the field. For example, if it is a surgical area, review the evidence base for pre-op care procedures and surgical wound infections.

- Identify specialist NICE guidelines and national standards relating to the field, as you may be questioned on these areas (especially for roles in bands 6–8), e.g.:
  - national KPIs (NHS England, 2019)
  - local evaluations/audits and recently published CQC reports
  - national escalation tools and pathways, e.g. NEWS2/PEWS escalation policy (Royal College of Physicians, 2017)
  - national risk assessment/incident reporting tools and guidelines, e.g. Mental Capacity Assessment and Deprivation of Liberty Safeguards (DoLS) (Mental Health Act, 2007).

## Current 'hot' topics:

- Review current topical issues within the profession across media and professional journals, as interviewers may ask you to discuss a contemporary practice-related subject.
- Attend national conferences, events and study days relating to the specialist field.
- Link to relevant online sites that disseminate field-specific information.

### 5.3.2  Structuring potential questions and preparing your responses

It is helpful to compose potential interview questions through your background research. One of the most effective ways to boost your performance during an interview is to prepare responses to these potential questions and to rehearse them. You do not have to memorise every answer word for word but you can use certain cases to jog your memory.

### Use bullet points, concise notes or mnemonics

Having bullet points and/or concise notes under each question, including key papers and practice examples, can help your recall during an interview or competency-based assessment. Some people, like me, will use simple trigger words or letters to prompt their memory. If I am asked about the use of evidence-based practice, for example, I will remember key words linked to evaluative projects that I have led, such as: 'Falls', 'Action learning' and 'Preceptorship programme', using the mnemonic 'FAP'. Under each project I will have some detail I remember such as the percentage of fall reduction and themes of programme evaluation. Third year students may use mnemonics to remember names of important placements and example cases that demonstrate developing skills.

### 5.3.3 Offer in-depth answers using examples

It is important to offer in-depth answers during your interview, including practical examples to demonstrate your skills (see *Section 5.2.2*). Spend time preparing examples to demonstrate key transferable skills, such as: communication; compassion; team working; promoting high quality/ standards; leading and managing care and dealing with conflict/challenges. Just one example for each theme will suffice and one comprehensive case may demonstrate several transferable skills.

A third year student may prepare case examples from their previous placements and course portfolio. It is helpful for experienced staff to keep reflections from case examples throughout their careers that they can call upon for NMC revalidation or future interviews. Always adhere to the NMC (2018a) *Code* and maintain patient and staff confidentiality when presenting your examples.

### 5.3.4 Key themes for questions

Although interviewers will word their questions differently, there are key themes that are usually included in any interview, whatever the band, such as:
- Are you the right person for the role/opportunity?
- Do you understand the role/opportunity you have applied for?
- Are you compassionate?
- Are you a good communicator/team player?
- Can you cope?
- Will you promote evidence-based practice and quality improvements?
- Will you manage and lead effectively?
- Are you safe? What would you do if...?

*Table 5.1* offers potential interview questions under these themes and practical tips to help inform your answers. The RCN also offers '*Sample interview questions for nurses and healthcare professionals*' on their website (RCN, 2019). Do not be afraid to ask senior colleagues about the types of questions you may be asked too, especially those who are already in the role you are striving for.

Table 5.1: *Example interview questions and tips*

| Theme | Example questions | Practical tips |
|---|---|---|
| **Are you the right person?** | • Tell me about yourself<br>• Tell me about your career so far<br>• What led you to this specialist field/role/course?<br>• Why should we offer you this opportunity?<br>• Tell me about your passions/interests<br>• What is your greatest achievement?<br>• How do you self-direct your learning and professional development?<br>• What are your strengths/weaknesses?<br>• Where do you see yourself in 5 years' time?<br><br>**Experienced band 5 and above:**<br><br>All of the above questions and:<br>• What service initiatives have you supported over the last year? | • Interviewers want to know that you are the right person for the role, i.e. you are competent, committed, enthusiastic, motivated and self-directed<br>• Broad open questions require concise and methodical answers – avoid rambling; your concise summary should include two key areas:<br>  – past roles/placements and academic and professional development – focus on your most recent/relevant achievement<br>  – commitment to the specialist area – how much the opportunity means to you; how it will inform your current/future practice; how you will influence care/the service/your profession<br>• Interviewers want an overview that relates to what you are applying for:<br>  – a 3rd year student may summarise previous acute/long-term placements but focus on skills developed during their 3rd year<br>  – experienced nurses may summarise past roles/achievements and focus on current projects that demonstrate leadership skills<br>• Highlight key achievements (see example projects in *Section 3.2.1*)<br>• When discussing a weakness, provide an explanation of how you manage it, e.g. *"I have very high standards and I like to deliver care myself, but I have learnt to prioritise and delegate effectively, as I cannot do it all"*<br>• When answering where you see yourself in 5 years' time, align your professional development and education to a career pathway (see *Section 1.3.2, Table 1.4*). If you are not sure where you will be, then be honest but aim to link to a career pathway over the next year at least. |
| **Do you understand what you have applied for?** | • Why have you applied for this specific role/course/scholarship?<br>• What are the main responsibilities of this role, and how will you prioritise them?<br>• What is your understanding of our Trust values and why are they important? | • Interviewers want to know that you understand what you are applying for and that you have made an effort to find out how a role/service/course/scholarship works<br>• Complete background research to fully understand what is being offered and what it involves |

| | | |
|---|---|---|
| | **Experienced band 5 and above:**<br>• What are the key differences between your current role and the role you have applied for?<br>• What will you find the hardest on this course? | • Demonstrate enthusiasm for the specialist field by highlighting:<br>– recent informal visits or contact with relevant staff<br>– attendance at specialist conferences/study days/recruitment events<br>– case examples demonstrating the development of key skills and/or project work in the field |
| **Are you compassionate?** | • How do you define compassion?<br>• Give an example where you recently provided compassionate care<br>• What hinders compassionate care? How would you overcome barriers to compassionate care?<br>• How do we prevent poor care, such as in the recent public inquiry into …?<br>• What would you do if you saw a staff member giving poor care to a patient? How do you escalate/report concerns or poor care standards?<br>• You may be given a scenario that involves signs of neglect or discriminating against a person. What are the signs of neglect in this situation?<br><br>**Experienced band 5 and above:**<br>• How will you assure the provision of compassionate care across our services? | • Interviewers aim to recruit individuals who are compassionate and who will escalate concerns regarding poor care standards. You should be able to define compassion with a related example. Alternative terms may be used, such as: *'person-centred'* or *'individualised'* or *'holistic'*. Ensure that you understand what all these terms mean too.<br>• Review summary reports/recommendations from public inquiries, such as:<br>– Winterbourne View Hospital public inquiry (DH, 2012)<br>– Mid Staffordshire NHS Foundation Trust public inquiry (Francis, 2013)<br>– Whorlton Hall independent review (CQC, 2019)<br>• Review escalation policies, the role of safeguarding leads, and how to report poor care standards<br>• Employers want assurance that you do not make judgements or label people, that you respect equality and diversity laws and you do not discriminate against a person's sex, gender, disability, sexual orientation, religion, belief, race or age<br>• Ensure that you understand the Equality Act (2010) and Disability Discrimination Act (1995) if called to discuss a scenario |
| **Are you a good communicator/ team player?** | • Give an example where you:<br>– dealt with a communication problem in the workplace<br>– supported a client/patient struggling to communicate<br>– dealt with a complaint<br>• How did you overcome challenges?<br>• What is your understanding of positive team working? Give an example | • Interviewers want to know that you are a good communicator and have the qualities to fit in with their service/team. Increase your self-awareness by reflecting on your current role and the roles of others, e.g. AHPs. Ask colleagues how they perceive your contribution. Students may use previous mentor feedback.<br>• Review Belbin's (2015) team roles to categorise your strengths/ weaknesses |

*Table 5.1: (continued)*

| Theme | Example questions | Practical tips |
|---|---|---|
| | • What type of team member are you?<br>• What strategies would you use to de-escalate if a patient/relative became angry with staff?<br>• What positive contribution can you offer the role/service/team? How will you use the course to benefit others/the service?<br><br>**Experienced band 5 and above:**<br>• How will you promote positive team working across our team/service?<br>• How would you deal with two team members refusing to work with each other? | • Reflect on verbal and non-verbal communication strategies that promote positive communication, therapeutic relationships and conflict resolution<br>• Understand the process of dealing with a complaint and the role of the Patient Advice and Liaison Service (PALS)<br>• Practice examples should promote positive team working that includes:<br>  – respect for others' views and collaborative working<br>  – willingness to overcome barriers to move forward positively<br>  – a caring, supportive and flexible approach<br>  – adherence to organisational/national policies and standards<br><br>**Experienced band 5 and above:**<br>• Review how to manage and lead challenging situations that require de-escalation skills and conflict resolution across a team/service |
| **Will you manage/lead effectively?** | • Give an example where you effectively managed/led a situation in practice? What skills did you use? What did you learn? How would you do things differently next time?<br>• How do you prioritise your caseloads?<br>• What is the difference between a manager and leader? What type of manager/leader are you?<br>• What is your management/leadership style?<br>• What would you do if you were unsure how to deliver.........aspect of care?<br><br>**Experienced band 5 and above:**<br>• How do you currently manage/lead staffing/low compliance/learning and development?<br>• Give an example where you have led a project in practice<br>  – What was the outcome?<br>  – Were there any barriers?<br>  – How did you overcome the barriers? | • Interviewers want to know that you are a safe practitioner who has the managerial and leadership skills required for the role/course, such as:<br>  – NQN/NQM/ODP – able to safely manage caseloads; assess, plan, implement and evaluate care; delegate to others and prioritise<br>  – band 6/7: uses change management models/tools to lead teams and innovate care that improves quality across a service<br>• Review the job description/person specification for key leadership and management skills required in the role<br>• Understand key health care terms relating to management and leadership (see *Table 3.5*)<br>• Review professional standards: NMC (2018a) *Code*; NMC (2018b) *Future Nurse*; NMC (2017b) *Standards for Competence for Registered Midwives*; NMC (2017a) *Practising as a Midwife in the UK*; and HCPC (2014) *Standards of Proficiency: operating department practitioners* |

| | | |
|---|---|---|
| | • How do you empower others to proactively lead in your clinical area? | **Experienced band 5 and above:**<br>• Understand different leadership styles/models/frameworks and identify practice examples where you have led a change and positively influenced care (see practice examples in Section 3.2.1). |
| **Will you cope?** | • Give an example where you overcame a challenging situation<br>• What personal strategies do you use to prioritise your workload?<br>• How do you know when you are becoming stressed? How do you prevent/manage stress?<br>• What will be the most worrying part of being a band X or being on this course?<br>• If you were worried about staffing on your shift what would you do?<br><br>**Experienced band 5 and above:**<br>• What strategies do you use to support colleagues who are showing signs of stress?<br>• How will you balance key service responsibilities with meeting the needs of your patients/clients?<br>• Talk me through how you will cope with ...... | • Interviewers want to know that you can cope with the demands of a job/course and that you can:<br>  – identify when you are becoming stressed<br>  – use strategies to prevent/manage stress<br>  – escalate concerns and ask for help<br>  – reflect on all of these areas and identify effective strategies and examples that demonstrate how you have overcome past challenges, e.g. through prioritisation, delegation and escalation<br>• Examine the job description for key responsibilities and areas of accountability<br>• Aim to understand organisational support structures to know how to access support (see Section 2.2.4)<br><br>**Experienced band 5 and above:**<br>• Understand local/national provision to support staff, such as: support groups/clinical supervision; HR services; employer assistance programmes; PIP and occupational health services |
| **Will you promote evidence-based practice and quality improvements?** | • How do you keep up to date?<br>• How do you ensure your practice is evidence-based?<br>• How do you promote quality care/high standards in your role?<br>• What does the term quality improvement/clinical governance/risk management/clinical audit mean to you?<br>• What is the difference between a policy, protocol and guidelines?<br>• Give an example from practice where you have delivered quality care? | • Interviewers want to know that you:<br>  – provide evidence-based care that meets national standards<br>  – act as a good role model to others<br>  – understand key terms relating to quality improvement<br>  – support quality improvement in your role<br>  – understand key terms and definitions relating to EBP (see Table 3.3) and improving quality of care (see Table 3.4) |

*Table 5.1: (continued)*

| Theme | Example questions | Practical tips |
|---|---|---|
| | **Experienced band 5 and above:**<br>• How would you lead the improvement of documentation standards across a team/service?<br>• Talk me through the change management model relating to a practice example | **Experienced band 5 and above:**<br>• Identify past clinical audits/CQC reports regarding standards in the area; if CQC report highlights low compliance rates regarding staff eLearning, then you may be asked how you would increase compliance rates<br>• Review national safeguarding directives and legislation; escalation and risk assessment standards and policies. Ensure that you understand key risk assessments linked to the specialist area. |
| **What do you do if?** | Often you will have a question:<br>*"What would you do if ……?":*<br>• … at 9 am you realise the night nurse has not signed for a 6 am IV antibiotic?<br>• … a controlled drug is missing?<br>• … you witnessed drug-taking by relatives?<br>• … you talk to a child visiting a patient who says they have been left alone all night?<br>• … a patient refuses their anti-convulsion medication and they have/do not have mental capacity?<br>• … a relative swears at an HCA and wants to make a complaint about the standard of care?<br>• … a patient suffering from dementia has gone missing from your unit?<br>• … you are worried about the safety of a vulnerable adult in the community?<br>**Experienced band 5 and above:**<br>• … team morale is low?<br>• …one of your junior staff is not meeting the requirements of their role? | • *"What would you do if ……?"* questions usually relate to an issue where you need to demonstrate:<br> – safe practice and working within professional boundaries/national standards<br> – good communication and/or team work<br> – appropriate escalation<br> – calmness and a methodical approach<br>• Review previous tips in the sections above for key reading and advice to answer related questions<br>• Answer scenario-based questions methodically using a systematic approach, such as the Nursing Process (Orlando, 1961) or an ABCDE approach (Resuscitation Council, 2015) for emergencies<br>**Experienced band 5 and above:**<br>• Use methodical leadership approaches to proactively deal with issues and to think 'globally' relating to scenarios |

*NOTE: All questions may be relevant to any band/field and additional questions are also presented for more experienced staff.*

## 5.4 ON THE DAY OF THE INTERVIEW

Following years of interviewing, I have known people to faint, break down sobbing and even laugh inappropriately during interviews, due to nerves. Most people become anxious before and during interviews, and it can also be nerve-racking waiting for a phone call to find out whether or not you were successful.

Within this section practical guidance is offered that aims to reduce additional stress, to help your interview go as smoothly as possible. A simple checklist is provided to help your preparation (see *Table 5.2*).

### 5.4.1 How early should I get there?

It is best to arrive too early, as opposed to a few minutes before your interview or even worse, late. You need time to compose yourself and calmly introduce yourself to interviewers. I would advise being within the vicinity an hour before your interview, to check that you are in the right part of a building. Arrive at the interview reception 20–30 minutes before your interview.

Always check in advance how long it takes to travel to the venue and allow extra time if you are relying on public transport out of area. Transport will not be accepted as an excuse for being late unless you have proof that it was cancelled or there was an accident.

Alternatively, you can request a Skype interview if you have to travel a distance, or it may be helpful to stay in a local hotel the night before.

### 5.4.2 What if I need to cancel?

If you need to cancel the interview due to sickness, bereavement or your train being cancelled, ensure that you contact the interviewers by phone and email as soon as possible. They may be able to rejig their schedules and offer you another interview date soon after. They are much more likely to offer an alternative if you cancel prior to the interview, rather than just not turning up.

Interviewers are not obliged to interview anyone who cannot make an interview and it is purely at their discretion and convenience as to whether you will be offered another slot. However, most interviewers will try their best to accommodate someone who has informed them as soon as they could about unforeseen circumstances.

### 5.4.3 *What should I take with me?*

There will be items that you need to take to your interview that may be easily forgotten on the day, such as:

- **details about venue:** bring full address/postcode and directions, in case your maps app goes down.
- **phone:** do not forget a charged mobile if you need to use a maps app. Make sure your mobile is switched off before the interview.
- **application documents:** bring your application reference number or invitation with details.
- **ID documents:** you may need the following: NMC PIN; passport; driving licence; work permit/visa; Disclosure and Barring Service (DBS) certificate, if requested. If in doubt, check with the local HR department. Do not worry too much if you forget documents on the day, as you always can come in on another date, if needed.
- **certificates:** some employers/universities request that professional/ academic certificates are brought to the interview.
- **hard copy of your professional portfolio:** you may wish to bring your professional portfolio (see *Section 4.5*).
- **questions to ask interviewers:** bring questions for the interviewers if you think you will forget, e.g. what orientation will the successful candidate be offered?; how do you support someone with dyslexia on this course?
- **sustenance for the day:** bring money and/or bank card and food/drink.

### 5.4.4 *What should I wear?*

Your clothes should be smart and clean, and you should wear comfortable clothing that is not too tight. A smart suit or jacket, shirt/blouse and trousers/skirt, or plain dress and shoes are ideal. If you do not have anything suitable and need to keep costs down, you can find many good quality clothes in charity shops. Navy or darker suits/jackets are good investments, as you can always wear them in future interviews.

Choose your outfit the night before to avoid panicking on the day. It is the worst feeling to find a stain on your clothing when you are due to attend an interview or find that you cannot fit in an outfit any more. You need a calm mindset and having your outfit ready is conducive to that.

Do not wear strong perfume/aftershave, as some people may be allergic.

### 5.4.5  How do I greet the interviewer?

Offer the interviewer a warm hello and smile and thank them for offering you the interview. You are aiming to achieve a balance between being approachable and coming across as over-confident.

First impressions count and if you do not know the interviewer, shake their hand during introductions, as long as you feel comfortable doing this. Avoid negative body language, such as: crossed arms; yawning; not looking at the interviewers when they are speaking to you (*they may think you are uninterested*); or slouching in your chair. You are aiming to look alert, bright and interested to answer questions.

### 5.4.6  How do I calm my nerves?

Interviewers always expect candidates to be nervous and good interviewers will try to calm you down at the start of your interview. Interviewers should want to get the best out of a candidate, not traumatise them!

Everyone has different methods to decrease their nerves; however, one of the most effective ways is to spend as much time as you can on preparation. The more preparation you do, the more confident you will feel on the day. You need to be mentally and physically prepared for your interview. Try to have a good night's sleep and do not take on too much in the days leading up to your interview.

Try to place the interview in context and just try your best. There will be other opportunities in the future and many staff, including me, have had unsuccessful interviews they would rather forget. Never think that you have blown an interview because one of the interviewers remains stony-faced throughout – they may be like that during all interviews or having a generally bad day.

Avoid chewing gum to calm your nerves, as this can create a bad impression.

### 5.4.7  What if I can't answer questions?

Remember, there is no rush to answer, and interviewers expect you to ponder on questions. If you feel you are unable to speak, just be honest and let the interviewer know you are nervous. They should be sympathetic, especially if you are newly registered. Band 5 interviews tend to be conducted in a friendlier atmosphere, due to high vacancy rates, so try not to panic. If you are unsure about what an interviewer is asking, then never be afraid to ask for further clarification.

Ask for a few moments to collect your thoughts and take a deep breath to think methodically about the questions. If you still cannot answer, then ask the interviewer if you can come back to the question later. Ideas may come to you as you progress through the interview.

When responding to questions, keep to what you know best and try to be as positive as you can, even if you cannot answer. A caring person will come across well in an interview, even if they stumble over words and cannot quite articulate everything clearly on every question.

## 5.5 AFTER THE INTERVIEW

At the end of your interview, it is acceptable to ask interviewers when you are likely to hear back from them and they should indicate a time frame.

After your interview you will be contacted by a lead interviewer, usually by telephone, and informed whether or not you were successful. If successful, you will be verbally offered a provisional position/course, pending normal HR checks. You will be asked whether you wish to accept the offer or decline it. If you choose to accept, a formal HR process will follow that includes reference checks (see *Section 4.2.8*) and occupational health clearance. Chasing up references can take weeks if your referee is on holiday. If you are worried about delays, do not hesitate to contact the HR department to put your mind at rest.

Once your references and occupational health have been cleared, you will be asked to sign a formal contract with your employer. If you have not signed a contract, you have no legal obligation to take up an offer and may change your mind and withdraw from a post with no contractual obligations. However, it is good practice to let potential employers know if you have applied for several posts or are unsure whether to take up their offer. Remember, you never know when you may meet a manager again and it is always best to act honestly and professionally in such situations.

---

### ☰ KEY TIP

- Remember, you never know when you may meet a manager again and it is always best to act honestly and professionally before, during and after your interview.

### 5.5.1  What if I receive more than one offer?

Receiving more than one offer is a great position to be in and there is nothing wrong with applying for several posts, as long as you can cope with multiple applications. Employers expect that some third year students will apply for more than one position, to widen their options.

You need to make a decision and choose one offer, as soon as you can. If you are unsure, compare what each area is offering:

- Do they offer a good induction/orientation?
- Does the field excite me?
- What future career pathways are available?
- Are there post-registration courses to help my progression?
- Are there educators to guide my development?
- Are current team/staff happy?
- Do they offer the shifts I need?

Always be open with employers if you have applied for more than one post, especially if you have several interviews near to each other. If you have another interview in a few days, employers may hold off contacting the other candidates and wait until you have attended and made your decision.

### 5.5.2  Dealing with rejection

I regularly offer support to individuals who were not successful following an interview. Some accept that the decision was made due to their performance, others were frustrated, questioning the calibre of other candidates who had less experience than them, or feeling that the interview panel was biased. My advice is always the same; it is divisive to focus on other applicants and is a waste of your energy. How can you be sure that you were the strongest candidate if you did not read the other candidates' applications and were not present for all the interviews? Do not blame the interviewers; instead, try to accept responsibility for your performance on the day. Focus on your future development and prepare as much as possible to increase your chance of success in the future.

### 5.5.3  Learn from your interview experience and feedback

After an unsuccessful interview, it is important to request feedback on your performance, to establish what you did well and to identify areas that require further preparation. You have been assessed by experienced staff and important insights may be gained from their feedback.

You are entitled to verbal feedback directly from one of the interviewers. Your feedback may be given by telephone or face to face. Employers are not obliged to give interviewees written feedback from their interviews. It helps to have specific questions prepared, such as, "*What was my strongest/ weakest answer?*" and/or "*What two areas would you say I needed to work on the most?*"

After your interview, write down the questions you were asked as soon as possible, in case you forget. You can use them to practise for future interviews.

 **KEY TIP**

- Offer to act as a future interviewer to increase your insights into the way candidates are assessed, e.g. a band 5 can act as an interviewer for nursing assistants (NAs), operating department assistants (ODAs) and band 4 nursing associates.

*Table 5.2:* Checklist to prepare for interviews

| BACKGROUND RESEARCH | | |
| --- | --- | --- |
| **To do** | **Tick** | **Notes** |
| Review type of interview/ assessments | | |
| Review role/course information | | |
| Review service/institution information | | |
| Review key healthcare terms and definitions | | |
| Review local and national standards | | |
| Review current 'hot' topics | | |
| STRUCTURING QUESTIONS AND RESPONSES | | |
| **To do** | **Tick** | **Notes** |
| Prepare interview questions & responses | | |
| Book mock interview/ alternative rehearsal | | |

*Table 5.2: (continued)*

| PREPARATION BEFORE INTERVIEW (DO NOT LEAVE UNTIL THE DAY!) | | |
|---|---|---|
| **To do** | **Tick** | **Notes** |
| Getting to venue: timings/ address/map/charge phone/ tickets | | |
| Interview outfit/shoes | | |
| *Application documents:* Reference number/invitation letter or email | | |
| *ID documents:* NMC PIN; passport, driving licence, work permit/visa; DBS certificate/other | | |
| Professional/academic certificates (if needed) | | |
| Professional portfolio | | |
| Questions for interviewers | | |
| Money/card and food/drink | | |

## WHAT TO DO NEXT

1. Increase your understanding of what a VBI is and how interviews are scored and rated according to your responses. Offer to be a member of a local interview panel to increase your insight into the whole interview process. Band 5s may interview nursing/midwifery assistants or associate nurses.
2. Once you have secured an interview, allocate a day or more of preparation time to prepare mentally and physically for your interview. Check the type of interview being used to know exactly what to expect on the day. If you are unsure about any aspect of the interview schedule, contact the lead interview/HR team for clarification.
3. Create an interview plan and checklist that includes: the completion of background research; structuring potential interview questions and responses; and preparing the logistics for the day of the interview.

4.  Carefully plan and prepare case examples to include in your responses to interview questions and rehearse your answers. Practical examples must demonstrate understanding of the question and focus on your contribution and the impact you made on a situation.
5.  Use bullet points, concise notes or mnemonics to help you remember case examples and key points in the interview.
6.  Arrange a mock interview if possible, to receive constructive feedback on your performance. Feedback should inform your interview preparation and improve your performance on the day.

## REFERENCES AND FURTHER READING

BBC News (2017) *Children Interrupt BBC News interview.* Available at: www.youtube.com/watch?v=Mh4f9AYRCZY [accessed 10 December 2019]

Belbin (2015) *Team Role Theory – Belbin Team Roles* (online). Available at: www.belbin.com/about/belbin-team-roles/ [accessed 10 December 2019]

Care Quality Commission (2019) *Update on Independent Review into Regulation of Whorlton Hall* (online). CQC. Available at: www.cqc. org.uk/news/stories/update-independent-review-regulation-whorlton-hall [accessed 10 December 2019]

Davison, N. (2020) *Numeracy and Clinical Calculations for Nurses,* 2nd edition. Lantern Publishing.

Department of Health (2012) *Transforming Care: a national response to Winterbourne View Hospital.* The Stationery Office. Available at: https://assets.publishing.service.gov.uk/government/uploads/system/uploads/attachment_data/file/213215/final-report.pdf [accessed 10 December 2019]

Disability Discrimination Act (1995). Available at: www.legislation.gov.uk/ukpga/1995/50/contents [accessed 10 December 2019]

Equality Act (2010). Available at: www.legislation.gov.uk/ukpga/2010/15/contents [accessed 10 December 2019]

Francis, R. (2013) *Report of the Mid Staffordshire NHS Foundation Trust Public Inquiry: executive summary.* The Stationery Office.

Health and Care Professions Council (2014) *Standards of Proficiency: operating department practitioners.* HCPC. Available at: www.hcpc-uk.org/globalassets/resources/standards/standards-of-proficiency---odp.pdf [accessed 10 December 2019]

Higgins, C.A. and Judge, T.A. (2004) The effect of applicant influence tactics on recruiter perceptions of fit and hiring recommendations: a field study. *Journal of Applied Psychology*, **89**: 622–632.

Jones, E. and Gordon, E. (1972) Timing of self-disclosure and its effects on personal attraction. *Journal of Personality and Social Psychology*, **24**: 358–365.

Lapham, R. (2015) *Drug Calculations for Nurses: a step-by-step approach*, 4ᵗʰ edition. Taylor & Francis/CRC Press.

Mental Health Act (2007) The Stationery Office. Available at: www. legislation.gov.uk/ukpga/2007/12/pdfs/ukpga_20070012_en.pdf [accessed 10 December 2019]

NHS England (2019) *Integrated Urgent Care Key Performance Indicators and Quality Standards 2018*. Available at: www.england. nhs.uk/wp-content/uploads/2018/06/integrated-urgent-care-key-performance-indicators-quality-standards-revised-050219.pdf [accessed 10 December 2019]

Nursing and Midwifery Council (2017a) *Practising as a Midwife in the UK*. NMC. Available at: www.nmc.org.uk/globalassets/ sitedocuments/nmc-publications/practising-as-a-midwife-in-the-uk.pdf [accessed 10 December 2019]

Nursing and Midwifery Council (2017b) *Standards for Competence for Registered Midwives*. NMC. Available at: www.nmc.org.uk/ globalassets/sitedocuments/standards/nmc-standards-for-competence-for-registered-midwives.pdf [accessed 10 December 2019]

Nursing and Midwifery Council (2018a) *The Code: professional standards of practice and behaviour for nurses, midwives and nursing associates*. NMC. Available at: www.nmc.org.uk/globalassets/sitedocuments/nmc-publications/nmc-code.pdf [accessed 10 December 2019]

Nursing and Midwifery Council (2018b) *Future Nurse: standards of proficiency for registered nurses*. Available at: www.nmc.org.uk/ globalassets/sitedocuments/education-standards/future-nurse-proficiencies.pdf [accessed 10 December 2019]

Nursing and Midwifery Council (2019) *Record Keeping Guidance*. Available at: www.nmc.org.uk/standards/code/record-keeping/ [accessed 2 January 2020]

Orlando, I.J. (1961) The Dynamic Nurse–Patient Relationship. G.P. Putnam's Sons: Penguin Adult.

Resuscitation Council UK (2015) *Resuscitation Guidelines 2015: the ABCDE approach*. Available at: www.resus.org.uk/resuscitation-guidelines/abcde-approach/ [accessed 10 December 2019]

Royal College of Nursing (2019a) *Royal College of Nursing Evidence to the NHS Pay Review Body 2018–19*. RCN.

Royal College of Nursing (2019b) *Sample Interview Questions for Nurses and Healthcare Professionals* (online). RCN. Available at: www.rcn.org.uk/professional-development/your-career/interviews/sample-interview-questions [accessed 10 December 2019]

Royal College of Physicians (2017) *National Early Warning Score (NEWS 2) Standardising the assessment of acute-illness severity in the NHS*. RCP. Available at: www.rcplondon.ac.uk/projects/outputs/national-early-warning-score-news-2 [accessed 10 December 2019]

Starkings, S. and Krause, L. (2018) *Passing Calculations Tests in Nursing: advice, guidance and over 400 online questions for extra revision and practice*. Sage.

# MOVE FORWARD POSITIVELY FROM CHALLENGES

*"Have no fear of perfection; you'll never reach it."*
Marie Curie (1867–1934), French physicist, chemist
and a pioneer in the study of radiation

## 6.1 LEARNING FROM YOUR EXPERIENCES

The chance to collaborate with different people across evolving healthcare environments is what makes our professions unique and fulfilling. However, collaborating with people using dynamic systems and processes may present challenges to a nurse or midwife. The human factors involved in healthcare mean that individual reactions and behaviours can differ, which can lead to effective practice and cohesive collaboration, or error and conflict in the workplace.

The above quote from Marie Curie is very apt when applied to managing challenges in healthcare. None of us will ever know it all and reach 'perfection', as services constantly evolve and new research adds to an ever-growing evidence base. We will all have times when we get it wrong or could have done things better, and lifelong learning is an inherent part of our professional development. Throughout your career, it is important that you learn to deal with changes in practice and learn to move forward positively from challenging experiences, to prevent the risk of stress-related illness.

It is difficult to thrive in your career and to develop professionally if you are experiencing stress, conflict or a lack of support at work. This chapter provides practical tips and guidance to help you constructively manage future challenges. Key areas are covered, such as:
- how to prioritise and access support
- how to use narrative and reflection to learn from your experiences
- how to prevent and manage stress
- how to resolve communication issues in the workplace.

The chapter begins with an overview of current workforce pressures and highlights the need for employers to take responsibility for supporting staff wellbeing in the workplace. Supportive national frameworks to retain staff are presented within this section for you to access or use to support others.

### 6.1.1 Workforce pressures

If you are practising as a nurse in the UK today, you are likely to be working across a pressurised service that is struggling to meet demands due to high staff vacancy rates and high staff turnover. In March 2019, the quarterly performance report by NHS Improvement revealed that the number of vacant nursing posts was 39 148, an 11% increase in comparison to March 2018 (Health Education England, 2018; NHS Improvement, 2019). The examination by Buchan *et al.* (2019) of NHS staffing trends in England over 2018 reported that NHS Trusts had a shortfall of more than 100 000 NHS staff, with more than 1 in 10 registered nursing posts being vacant. Current NHS vacancies have even been declared a 'national emergency' across media outlets, such as BBC News (BBC News, 2019).

Workforce projections in the future paint a similar picture. The joint workforce report *Closing the Gap: key areas for action on the health and care workforce*, a collaborative account from the Health Foundation, King's Fund and Nuffield Trust (2019, p. 2), states that: "On current trends, in 10 years' time the NHS will have a shortfall of 108,000 full-time equivalent nurses. Half this gap could be bridged by increasing the number of nurses joining the NHS from training. **This would require 5,000 more nurses to start training each year by 2021…**".

It is helpful for nurses and midwives to review current NHS plans and government papers to increase their knowledge of health service delivery proposals. By increasing your knowledge of health and social care plans, you may influence future change as part of a professional group. Having an awareness of current national policy will also inform future preparation for interviews, especially for band 6 roles and above.

### 6.1.2 Pre-registration applications and attrition rates

Evidence suggests that rising vacancy rates have been affected by the withdrawal of the NHS nursing bursary and high attrition rates on pre-registration courses, where 24% of those starting a nursing degree either do not graduate, or do not graduate within the expected time frame (Buchan *et al.*, 2019). In 2017 the number of applications to nursing degree courses fell by 18%, which coincided with the withdrawal of the

NHS bursary in England. The number of 'acceptances' on nursing degree courses in England also fell by 2.6%, whilst 'acceptances' in countries where NHS bursaries were maintained increased by 9.3% in Scotland and 6.2% in Wales (Buchan *et al.*, 2019). In July 2019, the RCN (2019c) website headlined with: 'Nursing degree application numbers still at crisis point after bursary removal' following figures from UCAS revealing that nursing applications had fallen by 29% since 2016. The RCN continues to campaign for the return of NHS bursaries for nurses in England.

To address workforce issues, initiatives such as the Health Education England (HEE) RePAIR project seek to reduce pre-registration attrition and improve staff retention (i.e. decrease student and staff leavers) (HEE, 2018). The HEE (2018) RePAIR toolkit promotes the sharing of good practice, buddy schemes and clinical practice educator posts, structured preceptorship and staff wellbeing programmes. Higher education institutions (HEIs) are expected to reduce student nurse attrition rates through collaboration with local providers and the widening of entry routes into nursing. The King's Fund (2019) agrees, suggesting that the "NHS needs to become more self-sufficient in training its own nurses" and there is an expectation that employers should grow their own trained staff using apprenticeship schemes.

It is helpful to check with your local employer how they are delivering the HEE (2018) RePAIR national recommendations and find out who is responsible for guiding your learning and development (see *Table 2.1*).

### 6.1.3 Staff leavers and NMC registrants

Working within challenging healthcare environments that are struggling to recruit and retain staff has undoubtedly led to nurses leaving the profession. The NMC (2017) reported that between 2016 and 2017, 27% more registrants left the register than joined. Encouragingly, in March 2019 the 'NMC Register Report' detected that the number of UK trained professionals registered had risen by 5000, in comparison to the same time the previous year. During the period 1 April 2018 to 31 March 2019, the NMC also reported that the number of midwives had increased by 500, which is in line with a constant increase in midwives over the last 5 years (NMC, 2019a). In January 2019 the first nursing associates were welcomed onto the NMC professional register and by July 2019, more than 1000 were registered as nursing associates (NMC, 2019b).

There is continued reliance on international recruitment across our health and social care services and during 2018–19 more than 6000 people joined the NMC register from outside Europe, compared to 3000 in the previous 12 months. In contrast, there was a decrease of 2000 in people joining the register who had trained in the European Union (NMC, 2019a).

Although the current upward trend in new NMC registrants is positive, it should be treated with caution, as movements are transient and remain too low to meet current workforce demands. The King's Fund's (2019) response to the interim NHS People Plan describes "years of poor workforce planning" and suggests an additional 5000 nurses a year need to be recruited "from countries with an over-supply of healthcare workers" in the short term, as training UK-based nurses would "take time to have an effect" (King's Fund, 2019).

## Keep up to date with national workforce and service delivery plans

Clearly, there is an urgent need to improve current and future staffing levels across health and social care services. The UK government has acknowledged that there is a "pressing need" to expand nursing workforce at "scale and pace" to meet service demands (House of Commons Health Committee, 2018). The Interim NHS People Plan (NHS England and NHS Improvement, 2019) sets out a vision to reduce nursing vacancy levels to 5% by 2028 to be able to deliver the NHS Long Term Plan over the next 10 years (NHS England, 2019a). However, there is much heated debate across the UK nursing press, professional online forums and Twitter calling for staffing issues to be resolved immediately, not by 2028.

Within the NHS Long Term Plan (NHS England, 2019a), there are radical changes planned across the NHS linked to the way we deliver care, such as:

- expanding non-hospital care services
- the launch of a digital NHS 'front door' using an NHS app
- reconfiguration of outpatient services to avoid up to a third of face-to-face outpatient appointments
- implementation of integrated care systems (ICSs) covering the whole country
- primary care networks of integrated multi-professional community teams (NHS England, 2019a).

Some of the visionary changes planned, if sufficiently staffed, may empower staff and patients in the future. Alternatively, if there are gaps in the workforce, changes may cause frustration amongst professional groups.

Only broad NHS long-term plans and timelines were released in 2019 (NHS England, 2019a); it is therefore important to keep up to date with future plans and developments. Future national health-related policies and government laws, Acts or papers will affect how we deliver health and social care. By increasing your insights about how national healthcare systems work and how decisions lead to health reforms, you may positively affect future policy through joining campaigns, collaborating with national consultations and conducting research to influence change (see *Section 7.2*). While healthcare professionals continue to deliver services under challenging circumstances, there are national campaigns trying to address staffing concerns, such as the RCN Safe Staffing Campaign, calling for safe staffing legislation in each UK country (RCN, 2019b). Workforce issues will inevitably affect your future job satisfaction, service delivery and standards of patient care. As you move up to higher banded roles, you may also be questioned on national workforce documents.

It is helpful to network using online information-sharing sites, as key documents are disseminated, summarised and discussed. You may wish to sign up to receive newsletters and alerts from national professional bodies, institutions and journals, and follow national Twitter groups, such as:

- Twitter accounts aimed at supporting students and registered staff:
  - @StNurseProject
  - @WeStudentNurses
  - @WeNurses
  - @WeLDnurses
  - @WeMHNurses
  - @WeMidwives
  - @WeCYPNurses
  - @CYPNAUK
  - @WeDistrictNurse
  - @RN_Community
  - @NurAssociates
- professional journal accounts releasing article abstracts:
  - *Nursing Times*: @NursingTimes: www.nursingtimes.net/
  - *Nursing Standard*: @NurseStandard: https://rcni.com/nursing-standard
  - *British Journal of Nursing*: @BJNursing: https://info.british journalofnursing.com/
  - *Journal of Advanced Nursing*: @jadvnursing: https://onlinelibrary. wiley.com/journal/13652648
  - *Journal of Clinical Nursing*: @jclinnursing: https://onlinelibrary. wiley.com/journal/13652702

- *Nurse Education Today*: @NurseEducToday: www.journals. elsevier.com/nurse-education-today
- *Health Service Journal*: @HSJnews: www.hsj.co.uk
- *British Journal of Midwifery*: @BJMidwifery: https://info.british journalofmidwifery.com
- *Midwifery Journal*: @MidwiferyJnl: www.midwiferyjournal.com/
- Midwives Information & Resource Service (MIDIRS): @MIDIRS: www.midirs.org/
- national institutions releasing key health-related documents:
  - The King's Fund: @TheKingsFund: www.kingsfund.org.uk
  - The Health Foundation: @HealthFd: www.health.org.uk/
  - Nuffield Trust: @NuffieldTrust: www.nuffieldtrust.org.uk
  - Department of Health and Social Care: @DHSCgovuk: www.gov.uk/
  - NHS Improvement and NHS England: @NHS Improvement and @NHS England: https://improvement.nhs.uk/
  - NHS Health Scotland: @NHS_HS: www.healthscotland.scot/
  - Public Health Wales: @PublicHealthW: www.publichealthwales. wales.nhs.uk/
  - Department of Health Northern Ireland: @healthdpt: www.health-ni.gov.uk/
- professional sites:
  - Royal College of Nursing: @RCN: www.rcn.org.uk/
  - Nursing and Midwifery Council: @nmcnews: www.nmc.org.uk/

## Resilience is not just about learning to 'get on with it'

It is widely acknowledged that you need to handle a certain level of stress to work as a nurse or midwife. The dynamic nature of healthcare interactions means that, realistically, you will always need to have a level of flexibility, problem-solving and decision-making under pressure. However, the amount of stress that is acceptable, and whether staff should be placed on resilience training courses, without government and employers taking responsibility for increasing workloads, is a matter of current debate within our profession.

Bright (1997) was the first to observe that nurses spent an inordinate amount of time caring for others, whilst not using a 'self-care approach' to develop 'personal resilience'. Resilience has been defined according to a variety of personal traits, such as tenacity and hardiness (Ablett, 2007; McGowan and Murray, 2016), resourcefulness, self-confidence and level-headedness (Giordano, 1997). Jackson *et al.*'s (2007) comprehensive literature review exploring the concept of personal resilience in nursing refers to resilience as: "the ability of an individual to adjust to adversity, maintain equilibrium, retain some sense of control over their environment, and continue to move on in a positive manner" (p. 3).

Jackson *et al.* (2007) identify a need for nurses to devise strategies to respond to workload stresses and build personal resilience, to prevent burnout. Overall findings suggest that nurses can develop and strengthen their own personal resilience to reduce their 'vulnerability to workplace adversity'. The authors suggest that personal strengths in nurses can be developed through strategies, such as: "building positive and nurturing professional relationships; maintaining positivity; developing emotional insight; achieving life balance and spirituality; and, becoming more reflective" (Jackson *et al.*, 2007, p. 1). Practical guidance relating to these strategies is covered later in this chapter (see *Section 6.2.4*). They also recommend integrating 'resilience-building' into nursing programme curriculums and offering professional support outside working environments using mentorship programmes.

An alternative perspective on resilience training from Teresa Chinn, a professional social media blogger for @WeNurses, set social media alight following her article entitled: 'Please don't call me "resilient"' (Chinn, 2018). Teresa called for our profession to stop pushing for staff to be resilient, "like a badge of honour", as individuals who are not coping may find it harder to ask for support and it turns "nurses into a scapegoat for systemic failings".

In summary, it may be useful to attend local resilience training courses that can provide helpful strategies to help you cope in a busy workplace environment. However, it is important to talk to experienced staff if you feel you are struggling and you should not just 'get on with it'. There is a need for future research examining the impact that resilience training may have on individuals' thoughts, feelings and practice experiences.

### ☰ KEY TIP

- Although nurses and midwives need to handle a certain level of stress, developing resilience is not about having an endless capacity to cope and to overcome workplace stresses; you can look more deeply into what may be causing workplace issues and make suggestions to improve work practices to relieve pressures for the whole team.

## 6.2 PRACTICAL ADVICE TO HELP YOU MOVE FORWARD FROM CHALLENGES

### 6.2.1 Be proactive and prioritise your support

Employers and universities have a duty of care to support the educational needs and wellbeing of their staff and students. However, it is important that you proactively take responsibility for your own professional development, support and health too. Managers may unintentionally miss signs that you are struggling, especially if you do not share your feelings with them. Some practical tips are presented below to help you proactively prioritise your support:

- Never be afraid to speak to a professional about your feelings if you are struggling at home or in the workplace. Most experienced staff I know, including me, have had times in their career when they have felt overwhelmed or unable to cope with a situation without the support of others. You manage to move forward from challenges by talking and offloading to colleagues and seeking expert advice.
- All institutions will have local department, divisional or corporate leads you can contact. Establish how corporate managerial and educational structures work and use local and national communication systems to access support (see the 'accessing support' list in *Step 2*).
- Proactively book regular time in advance to talk through issues with others, such as: your preceptor or clinical buddy, if you are newly qualified, or your clinical supervisor/assessor, line manager, lead educator or coach, if you are experienced in your role.

### 6.2.2 Use reflective writing

Talking to an experienced staff member or professional expert can help to decrease feelings of stress and anxiety at work. However, sometimes conversations within clinical environments lack depth and become too brief, emotive or reactive, due to the lack of time available. In such cases, individuals may use written accounts and reflections to help them analyse and evaluate situations in more depth. Various psychological research studies support the use of writing about your thoughts, feelings and life goals to increase your physical and psychological wellbeing, self-esteem and happiness (King, 2001; Spera *et al.*, 1994; Zech and Rimé, 2005; Zech, 1999).

Throughout your pre-registration degree you will have been encouraged to regularly use reflective frameworks in assignments or as part of clinical supervision groups, such as those of Johns (1995), Gibbs (1988) or Bulman and Schutz (2008). The process of reflection (a period of thinking) allows you to make further sense of an issue or situation by relating it to other experiences and theories, to place it in context (Gibbs, 1988; Bulman and Schutz, 2008). The six stages of the reflective cycle are presented in *Table 3.2*. Following registration, it is helpful to carry on using a reflective cycle to structure your thoughts into a positive plan of action. You may prefer to reflect on your own or find it helpful to share certain reflections with experienced colleagues for further guidance.

Oelofsen's (2012) book *Developing Reflective Practice* explores the role of narrative and use of reflection in front-line practice, where the demands of different agencies and services may conflict with an individual's needs. A helpful toolkit of reflective techniques is provided that include Oelofsen's 'Three-Step (CLT) Reflective Cycle' to build practitioners' reflective skills (see further details of the CLT reflective cycle in *Table 3.2*).

 **KEY TIP**

- You will need to provide five written reflective accounts for NMC revalidation every three years, and you can submit your reflections via NMC Online when your revalidation is due.

Some NQNs/NQMs have an intense dislike of reflective essays that puts them off using the reflective cycle when they qualify, whereas others are happy to maintain their reflective writing. Try to remember that your reflections are not being marked or critiqued and you can use any format or headings you prefer. See *Figure 6.1* for some simple questions to help you move a problem, issue or situation forward through the different stages of reflection. If you prefer to use a diary to order your thoughts and analyse your experiences, that is fine too. However, try to end your diary accounts on a positive note when possible and write a few actions to help you resolve issues if they arise again in the future, e.g. review an evidence base or seek additional support.

Our memories of positive experiences can easily be wiped out by negative experiences that we may dwell on, worry about or over-analyse. Using narrative to focus on the positive aspects of your life has been found to have psychological and physical health benefits, such as: promoting a positive mood; "fewer health centre visits for illness" (Burton and King, 2004; Emmons and McCullough, 2003); and reduced cholesterol levels (Floyd *et al.*, 2007). Reflecting on a positive experience may help individuals become more optimistic and promote constructive thinking; therefore, aim to include a regular positive reflection at the end of the day/week/month, where possible (see *Figure 6.2* for an exercise to help promote positive thinking).

| Questions to help you reflect on a problem/situation/issue |
| --- |
| 1. Describe your problem/situation/issue from practice |
| 2. What is your involvement in this problem/situation/issue? |
| 3. Why is this problem/situation/issue important to you? |
| 4. What do you feel are the reasons for this problem/situation/issue? |
| 5. What difficulties do you predict in tackling this problem/situation/issue again in the future? |
| 6. What do you feel may help you solve this problem/situation/issue? |
| 7. How will you recognise progress on this problem/situation/issue? |
| 8. How do you plan to deal with this problem/situation/issue if it arises again in the future? |

*Figure 6.1: Questions to help you reflect on a problem/issue/situation from practice.*

| Date: |
|---|
| 1. Start by thinking back over the day or last week/month. Focus on the positive experiences you have had. It may help to think about some of the following: <br> • Positive communications/interactions or relationships you have with others <br> • Encouraging feedback you have received or given to others <br> • Something new you achieved or did really well <br> • Something kind that someone did for you or you did for them <br> • A feeling of contentment when you were able to relax or enjoy life |
| 2. Write down three things that went really well for you: |
| **a)** ................................................................................................................................... |
| **b)** ................................................................................................................................... |
| **c)** ................................................................................................................................... |
| 3. Write a brief description of each experience and how it made you feel: |
| **a)** |
| **b)** |
| **c)** |

*Figure 6.2: An exercise to promote positive thinking.*

### 6.2.3  Look out for signs of stress in yourself and others

The rise in staff vacancies and registrants leaving the NMC register has clearly been linked to an increase in individuals experiencing workplace stress. During the period May to October 2018, the NMC (2019a) surveyed 3504 people to ask them why they left the NMC register. Survey findings indicated that 30% of respondents' top reason for leaving was due to "too much pressure leading to stress and/or poor mental health".

Understandably, 'Brexit' was the second most common reason elicited from people who trained in another EU country.

Similarly, the Health and Safety Executive (HSE) (2018) annual statistics identified that the average prevalence rate for work-related stress, depression or anxiety across all industries was 1320 cases per 100 000 workers, whereas health and social workers have a significantly higher rate of 2080 cases per 100 000 (HSE, 2018). Current available figures from NHS Digital (2019), during the period July 2018 to March 2019, reveal that NHS staff took almost 100 000 more days off due to stress than they did six years ago and in the field of acute medicine the number of sick days increased by 35% (NHS Digital, 2019).

Due to current workforce pressures, it is important that you learn to monitor your stress levels at work and learn to look out for increasing signs of stress in yourself and others. There is no shame in acknowledging that you feel stressed and unable to cope. These feelings may be transient if you seek support when needed, exercise self-care early on, and learn to develop strategies to prevent and manage your stress levels.

## What are the signs of stress?

It is important to be aware of signs of stress such as: a feeling of being 'out of control'; an inability to cope; and becoming more withdrawn, tearful, indecisive, irritable, depressed or aggressive towards others. Stress may also cause physiological effects such as: stomach ulcers; insomnia; hypertension; indigestion; nausea; headaches; hyperventilation; palpitations; and depression or chronic fatigue. A person may experience a lack of sexual libido and resort to smoking or consuming excessive amounts of alcohol or drugs, as they struggle to cope.

We will all have times in our life when we are more at risk of stress, such as when we feel:

- unsupported and/or alone in the workplace or at home
- pressurised to complete additional tasks by managers, employers, others or ourselves
- overloaded by extra commitments at work/home, e.g. feeling responsible for other team/family members
- unable to meet deadlines, e.g. complete work projects or academic assignments on time
- upset by others who promote conflict or who do not want to resolve a communication issue
- unable to cope with financial problems, sickness, bereavement or a divorce/relationship break-up.

During stressful times in our life, it is helpful to do four simple things:
1. Prioritise essential or urgent tasks at work and home
2. Don't take on any extra commitments
3. Use any network of support available to you
4. Request extensions to any deadlines you have.

## What is burnout?

Burnout is a state of physical and mental exhaustion that is caused by excessive or prolonged stress, often related to chronic occupational stress. It may be characterised by the following three features: exhaustion, cynicism and reduced ability to perform at work (Freudenberger, 1974; Lee and Ashforth, 1990; Maslach and Leiter, 2016).

- **Exhaustion:** the person may feel completely drained, tired and overwhelmed all the time, even when carrying out routine tasks. They may lose concentration and motivation easily or become withdrawn and stop communicating with their colleagues or family/friends.
- **Cynicism:** the person may start to resent their job and display signs of anger and frustration at work/home, which is out of character for them.
- **Reduced ability to perform at work:** the person may be unable to meet the demands of their role and/or fall behind with commitments and set deadlines. Other people may complain about their performance or they may start omitting essential care and making mistakes at work.

If you start to experience any signs of stress this is a warning that you need to do something about your situation and health. Otherwise, if it is left unmanaged, you may be at risk of future burnout and chronic health issues. Talk to someone you trust about how you are feeling and always seek advice sooner, rather than later.

Oelofsen (2012) highlights the importance of reflecting on stressful work-based situations to prevent the risk of burnout. He provides various exercises which aim to help individuals and/or a reflective practice group make sense of emotionally demanding situations within a professional context. Reflection in groups may promote positive team working and enable individual team members to feel confident and competent when confronted with challenging situations in the workplace.

We all have a responsibility to look out for colleagues who may be displaying signs of stress. Offering individuals our time, listening to their feelings, treating them with kindness and compassion, may be all they need to get them through a tough time. If you are worried about a colleague, encourage them to speak to others and make them aware of the support and services available that have been detailed throughout this chapter.

## Prioritise mental health support

The Mental Health Foundation (2019) reports that nationally 1 in 6.8 people are experiencing mental health problems at work at any given moment, and 12.7% of sickness absence days can be attributed to mental health conditions. Health service employers and universities supporting pre-registration student placements should prioritise support for staff and students in the workplace, to reduce the risk of stress and deterioration in mental health.

Remember, it is always OK to say you are struggling with your mental health and to ask others for help, whether you are a student starting out in your career or a newly registered or experienced manager. Some pointers to support you are shown below:

- Reputable institutions will provide support to staff and students through their experienced supervisory teams and occupational health department, who may suggest referral to a GP, psychotherapist or counsellor.
- Most universities have dedicated student support advisors, student counsellors and mental health support teams that you can contact through your Student Union.
- Often universities offer a number of free counselling and online therapies, such as cognitive behavioural therapy (CBT) courses that students can access from home if needed, along with free stress management workshops.
- You may wish to self-refer to counselling support services through your GP and local hospital or walk-in centre.
- Online information and helpful resources are also available for staff and students from a variety of UK national institutions and charities, such as:
  - Employee Assistance Online
  - Mind
  - Mindful Employer
  - Student Minds
  - Mental Health at Work
  - Heads Together.
- Heads Together in partnership with Mind introduced the Workplace Wellbeing Programme, which consists of two key elements:
1. *Employer gateway*: an online portal containing resources to enable employers to proactively and constructively address workplace mental health.

2. *Online SME (small and medium-sized enterprises) employee training*: to provide employees with workplace mental health training to enable them to support themselves and colleagues.

- HEE recently launched an NHS Health and Wellbeing Framework, which includes a diagnostic tool to help NHS organisations plan and implement their approach for improving staff health and wellbeing (HEE, 2018). If you manage teams of staff or work in a supportive role, it is helpful to review the local and national frameworks and toolkits available to support your colleagues. The NHS Health and Wellbeing Framework aims to:
  - create a healthy and supportive working environment
  - educate and upskill staff and line managers to be able to support staff
  - give staff access to interventions to improve their wellbeing and mental health.
- If you require urgent help and feel that your mental health has deteriorated you should always talk to someone; call your GP to book an urgent appointment. Call 111 out of hours to have access to a GP in a walk-in centre.
- Never suffer in silence, as there is always someone you can reach out to for help and support. You may also find it helpful to talk confidentially to the following charities:
  - Samaritans: telephone helpline available 24 hours a day, 7 days a week, tel: 116 123, Twitter: @Samaritans
  - CALM: telephone helpline and webchat service 7 hours a day (5 pm to midnight), 7 days a week, tel: 0800 585858, Twitter @theCALMzone and online webchat service: www.thecalmzone. net/help/webchat/
  - Mind: online resources from info@mind.org.uk, telephone helpline open 9 am to 6 pm, Monday to Friday (except bank holidays), tel: 0300 123 3393 and text: 86463.

### 6.2.4  Use strategies to prevent and manage stress

As a nurse or midwife it is important that you learn to identify strategies to prevent stress and manage stressful situations. This does not mean that you should have an endless capacity to cope with stress (see *Section 6.1.3*). Practical guidance is presented below, which includes accessing support from your line manager and local employer.

### Increase your awareness of stress triggers

When you first qualify you may find managing a caseload, completing band 5 competencies, delegating to junior staff or planning a safe discharge particularly stressful. An experienced manager may find performance managing a team member, leading clinical governance meetings or dealing with admin stressful. We are all individuals and different stressors will affect different people.

Effective stress management starts with identifying the sources of stress that trigger a stress response in you:

- What triggers start to make you feel stressed?
- Are there areas of practice that make you feel more stressed than others?
- Write a list of the top three things that are currently making you feel stressed at work.

We usually have two kinds of stressors:

1. **External stressors** come from elsewhere and 'happen to us', such as your working environment being short-staffed or having hundreds of emails to deal with as a manager on a Monday morning.
2. **Internal stressors** link to our attitudes and beliefs, such as fears, opinions and the high expectations we place on ourselves.

### Develop personal strategies to manage your stress triggers

Over your career you will develop strategies to manage both external and internal stressors through:

- seeking support from others
- role-modelling experienced professionals
- reflecting on practice
- reviewing an evidence base
- receiving constructive feedback and structured professional development
- post-registration education, such as: leadership; stress management; conflict resolution; specialist care and assertiveness courses
- escalating and reporting local issues to receive support and inform change.

There will always be someone responsible for your learning and professional development throughout your career. Managers, educators and employers have a responsibility to guide your training, education and development, which includes **helping you to develop the skills to manage your stress triggers** (see *Section 2.3*).

Start by sharing your stress trigger list with an experienced staff member whom you trust. Seek their advice as to how to deal with these triggers and review the current evidence base relating to any areas of practice you need to develop.

### KEY TIPS

- If you are finding it stressful delegating your caseload when you qualify, start by identifying patients' priorities and establishing timelines for key nursing tasks with an experienced staff member/local educator.
- Ask for constructive and honest feedback on how you are currently delegating your caseload. Your preceptor/practice supervisor may help you identify different strategies to help you delegate and prioritise.
- An educator may help you develop SMART goals or suggest relevant in-house courses.
- You may review the evidence base regarding how to delegate in practice and use common mnemonics, such as: the 5 Rs (Rights of delegation – Burke, 2019); the 4 Cs (Communication of initial direction – Zerwekh *et al.*, 1997) and the 7 Ks (What you need to 'know' when delegating in practice as a newly qualified nurse – Forde-Johnston, 2018).

## Aim to increase your knowledge, skills and competence in weaker areas

We all have areas of practice that we struggle with and we sometimes avoid. These areas often relate to our stress triggers. If you found presenting stressful as a student, for example, you are likely to be stressed at the thought of presenting in work-related meetings when you qualify.

Investing time targeting areas where your knowledge is lacking is invaluable. Completing a short City and Guilds teaching certificate or observing experienced presenters will inevitably develop your presentation skills and confidence, if this is your stress trigger.

## Learn to adapt to change

Learning to adapt to change and being flexible are essential skills for you to have, and they take time to develop when you qualify or change roles.

- Access supervision and support from experienced staff and educators if you are finding it hard adapting plans in your role.

- Spend time with senior staff, caseload/bed managers and ward/ floor/community coordinators to gain a more global perspective of leadership and management in your area.
- Attend leadership and managerial post-registration courses to increase your knowledge and help you manage and inform organisational change in the future (see *Section 2.3.5*).

## Try to keep things in perspective

It is easy to 'beat yourself up' and be overly self-critical, especially if you are newly qualified or starting a new band. Don't be hard on yourself if you feel stressed or under pressure, as everyone feels the same when new in post.

It is important that you share your feelings to keep things in perspective. You will not be the only NQN/NQM who is struggling on qualification, or manager who is struggling with new organisational responsibilities. Join local and national groups and network with others in the same role, as it helps to share ideas and contextualise your practice experiences.

## There are 24 hours in a day so learn to say no

You cannot do it all and sometimes our stress triggers are due to the pressure we place on ourselves, as we have high standards or we do not like the feeling of not completing tasks.

Over the years I, for one, have had to learn to compromise and to delegate or request longer deadlines. There will always be essential and urgent tasks but we work in teams and should always feel able to ask for additional support or say no when we need to.

Through discussing issues at work, you can utilise the experience of others to feel confident to say no, if appropriate. During a study day on stress management I was moaning about the inordinate quantity of emails I was receiving every day. One of the presenters went through how to manage emails and helped me identify strategies to prevent my stress trigger, such as: only looking at my emails once a day; not looking at emails at home; being clear on email responses I wished to receive; and not feeding inappropriate discussions on email that generate several responses. All these measures reduced the stress I felt before opening my computer on a Monday morning.

## Don't take on additional responsibility without considering what it will entail

Don't move up the career ladder into a new role, or commit to a future course, or offer to take on a new project, without knowing exactly what it will entail. Take time to reflect on whether you can handle the extra responsibility and time commitment required. You can always ask experienced staff for advice if you are unsure and often another opportunity will become available at a more suitable time.

It is better to delay courses or stay in your current role if you are uncertain. Does it really matter if you postpone applying for a band 6 or 7 for another year, if you are happy and are continuing to develop your leadership skills as an experienced band 5 or 6? If you feel ready for additional responsibilities then go for it, but if the time is not quite right due to your current circumstances, then wait.

## Focus on what you can change and not on the areas you have no control over

Try not to dwell on the negative and areas that are out of your control; for example, there may be no higher bands on offer when you are unhappy in your current role. Instead concentrate on improving your current situation. You can request additional support from managers or train band 5/6s to help you with projects, until a suitable post becomes available.

 **KEY TIP**

- Never compare yourself to others who are progressing more quickly than you, as everyone's personal journey will be different.

Remember there are many job opportunities and career pathways available for nurses and midwives across the UK. You have the power to change your situation and no one needs to be stuck in a job unhappy for long periods. Seek career advice and line up another job; life is too short to spend 8–12 hours a day miserable at work!

## Always prioritise your physical and mental wellbeing above anything work-related

It is important that you 'switch off' and enjoy your days off. However, regularly staying out late and abusing your body means you are more likely to make bad decisions and experience burnout. You need to self-care and make time to relax, keep fit and eat and sleep well.

Make sure you take breaks at work and if your manager/coordinator tells you to go for break, then go, as someone else should cover your workload.

See also the previous section on prioritising mental health support.

## Seek reasonable adjustments or a return to work plan

If you are experiencing stress-related symptoms at work, book to meet your manager and explain how you feel. Your manager should offer a confidential discussion, structured support and be open to reasonable adjustments, if indicated.

If an employer is aware of a health condition, such as chronic stress, they have a legal duty to consider making reasonable adjustments to support an individual. Reasonable adjustments may include: allowing time off to attend medical appointments; removing tasks that cause stress; and offering flexible working, reduced working hours and structured supervision.

You may wish to contact HR or occupational health advisers for additional support and explore the possibility of a therapeutic return or phased return to work plan.

- **A therapeutic return to work** plan allows the employee to keep in touch with managers and the workplace while off, through informal meetings and catch-ups.
- **A phased return to work** plan allows the employee to gradually return to work over an agreed period, e.g. starting with a few hours a week and building up to more hours over time. Return to work plans are agreed between the member of staff, their line manager and the HR department.

You may also benefit from a referral to a rapid access team, which is a fast-tracking system that secures rehabilitation and occupational health treatment for NHS staff to help their recovery.

## 6.2.5 Aim to resolve communication issues in the workplace

In life there will always be certain people you would rather not socialise with and personalities that clash with your own. In society you would walk away or not pick up the phone; however, at work you cannot do this when caring for members of the public and working across healthcare teams.

Managing interpersonal conflicts is an essential part of your role and relatively minor interactions can escalate if frustrations are left unresolved. Situations can worsen to the point where there are failing standards of care, such as those reported in the *Mid Staffordshire NHS Foundation Trust Public Inquiry* (Francis, 2013).

Many employers offer programmes to defuse or 'de-escalate' conflict in the workplace, e.g. 'conflict resolution' or 'de-escalation' training. Staff may also be offered 'assertiveness' study days to develop their confidence, or teams may be offered away days to promote positive team working. It is helpful to discuss any challenging communication issues you have experienced at work with local managers/educators and ask what training is available to you. Further tips and guidance relating to promoting collaboration and positive team working are presented below:

## Active listening

- Always use active listening and aim to understand the other person's view.
- Listening to the other person gives you more control, rather than reacting emotively to what they say.
- Pay attention to what the other person is saying, acknowledge their view and then inform them of your view, e.g. "*I understand why you have told me to do this* ..........; *however, I feel like this* ........, *and I need to make you aware of this* ..................". You are taking control and saying how you feel, whilst clearly asserting your views.

## Open problem-solving

- If you do not share honest feelings with the person/group they will never know your viewpoint and you may eventually become frustrated.
- Take a problem-solving approach to the situation and think about what you are trying to get across (use the reflective questions in *Figure 6.1* to guide you).

## Do your research when you are trying to get a point across to others

Arguments prevail through an evidence-based viewpoint underpinned by facts. It is not just about 'winning arguments' when you are trying to assert yourself. However, having a clear, factual informative discussion, timelines and/or documentation will help support your perspective, especially if it is something you feel strongly about.

- Practise being assertive, if you have a particularly difficult situation to address, and run through what you are going to say beforehand.
- Check if others are feeling the same and constructively try to sort out issues together as a team.

### Promote positivity from the start

- Try to book a meeting with the person/team in a calm and quiet environment to prevent interruptions.
- Thank the person/team at the start of the conversation for meeting with you. Starting a conversation in a positive manner is much better than launching into a rant.
- Even if the other person launches into a tirade it does not mean you have to. Listening to others venting their frustrations is a more powerful social position to hold than joining in, and allows you time to plan an informed reply later.

### Learn to compromise and see the wider picture

In the workplace you are one of a number of employees, which means you need to develop patience and a global view of situations.

It is easy to jump in and become angry when your needs are not met, without finding out what is happening across a team or service.

Sometimes two people have very different viewpoints and a compromise needs to be sought. Talk through issues with an experienced nurse in a confidential supervision session. Senior nurses and HR staff can also offer confidential mediation between staff members.

### Avoid extreme reactions

- Always try to keep calm and professional.
- Avoid emotive accusations and aggressive language by keeping to the facts.
- Plan what you are going to say before an important conversation/ meeting, as you are more likely to stick to the brief.

### Take control if you feel uncomfortable

Working in a pressurised work environment means that people sometimes become frustrated. They may be frustrated at a situation and take it out on the nearest person, so try not to take this personally.

You have the right to take control of a situation that is making you feel uncomfortable, by stopping the conversation. Acknowledge that you can see the person is frustrated and suggest that you continue the conversation later when the person has calmed down. You are taking control, not allowing them to continue to vent at you, setting clear boundaries and offering to resolve the situation at a later stage. This demonstrates a professional and assertive approach.

If you feel yourself becoming frustrated, try to take time out to calm down.

Remember, saying nothing is sometimes the best option rather than saying something that you may regret later. You can always come back to an issue later when you have had time to reflect on what has upset you and can call on experienced colleagues to support you.

## Look out for signs that a situation may escalate

Key signs that indicate a situation may escalate include:
- individuals appearing agitated, raising their voice, swearing or directly threatening others
- individuals invading personal space, finger pointing/increasing their gesticulations or standing over someone who is sitting down
- individuals starting to pace up and down, clenching fists and stiffening their body
- individuals appearing frightened, confused or disorientated
- individuals smelling of alcohol or showing signs of drug use, e.g. pinpoint pupils/slurred speech
- individuals being violent, throwing objects or attempting to push/ throw punches or items.

## Decrease the risk of harm if a situation is escalating

- Never put yourself/others at risk and always ask for help from colleagues, senior staff and/or medics when dealing with unpredictable situations.
- Whenever there are signs that a person's behaviour or situation has the potential to escalate, you should call for help earlier rather than later.
- Establish what security is available to you and the correct numbers. In any hospital/institution environment there should be on-call security and a bleep system for emergencies. Many reception areas have security numbers near to phones and/or placed on the back of staff ID cards.
- In a community setting adhere to lone working policies and individual emergency call systems if doing home visits.

- In any working environment police can be called if situations become dangerous.
- Never go into a quiet room on your own with a person who is showing signs of aggression, even if they have calmed down and you feel safe.
- Ask another member of staff to be present with you and leave the door open or talk to them in a public space. If you find yourself in a room with the person, position yourself near to the door to prevent anyone barricading you in.

## Promote positive team working

If you clash with a member of staff and feel an atmosphere developing, it is best to talk it through with them and let them know how you feel in a professional and honest manner, as soon as possible.

Initiate conversations in a quiet room and not in front of an audience. Listen to their perspective. You may not be best buddies but can aim for a professional relationship in the future.

Mediation can be offered between you and others if you cannot resolve an issue on your own. HR staff or a senior nurse/union representative can help mediate to ensure a positive conclusion.

Miscommunication across teams can escalate when others gossip and spread mistruths or information is shared second/third hand. Don't gossip about other people and if you hear others gossiping in your team, challenge them: how would you feel if they were talking about you in this way? It causes undue stress for the individuals being gossiped about and prevents positive team working.

If you feel you are being bullied at work, or witness others being bullied in the team, escalate your concerns to a senior manager and/or HR adviser. Encourage the person being bullied to talk to someone senior and offer to go with them to report it. Employers should adhere to local 'bullying and harassment at work' policies and guidelines.

## Deal with complaints from patients or relatives as soon as possible

Usually complaints start off as a simple question or problem, but can quickly escalate if they are not handled empathetically and professionally at the time.

- Use open, clear language and posture that suggests an honest and sympathetic approach.

- Give the person your undivided attention and never be confrontational and answer back in annoyance or raise your voice. Talk to the person in a quiet place with seating and not at a busy desk with lots of commotion.
- Give the person your name, role and state you are there to help them.
- Establish why the person is complaining and try to put yourself in their shoes, e.g. are they grieving or has an operation been cancelled numerous times?
- Try to put it right with realistic timelines; however, never offer to sort problems out if you have no means to do so, e.g. do not state that you will inform the doctor or will be back in five minutes, and not return. Often complaints escalate when the person feels let down and not listened to.
- Focus on problem-solving and avoid 'passing the buck' or blaming others. If you cannot resolve a problem/complaint quickly, escalate to your seniors.
- Apologise, if the person has a valid complaint, e.g. *"I am very sorry you feel that the care has been poor; shall we discuss your concerns in the quiet room to plan how we can improve the situation?"*

A written apology from the service manager should be given if it is recognised that something has gone wrong. Usually the patient and their family/significant others will have a chance to discuss their complaint with the key service lead.

Ensure you adhere to local complaints policy. Advise a patient/family to complain formally through PALS or give them the name/contact details of the lead manager/head of service. Information should come from one lead, to prevent conflicting information.

The local policy for managing complaints should be adhered to and the complainant should also have a copy. Make a record of what happened in the patient's notes, what you said and any actions taken, using the clinical incident reporting system.

### You won't get it right all the time

Never beat yourself up about a situation you feel went badly, as no one gets it right every time. Every senior nurse or midwife can recall dealing with a past communication issue they would rather forget.

Remember, it is those thousands of interactions you have during your career that build your skills and enable you to handle future situations so you can become a role model to others!

—————————————— **WHAT TO DO NEXT** ——————————————

1. Review national health-related policies and government Acts or papers that affect how health and social care is delivered across the UK. You may be questioned on key papers relating to workforce strategy in future interviews for management roles.

2. Access online information-sharing sites, where professional documents are disseminated, summarised and discussed. Sign up to receive newsletters/alerts from professional bodies, institutions and journals. Follow national Twitter groups aimed at supporting students and professionals. Consider joining national campaigns and collaborating with consultations to positively influence professional change and health-related policy.

3. Access clinical supervision from experienced staff and educators. Book regular time in advance to talk through concerns and issues with others, such as: your preceptor or clinical buddy, if you are newly qualified; or your clinical supervisor/assessor, line manager, lead educator or coach, if you are experienced in your role.

4. Use reflective writing to structure your thoughts into a positive plan of action. Share reflections with experienced colleagues for further guidance. Aim to include a regular positive reflection at the end of the day/week/month, to promote positive thinking.

5. Spend time with senior staff, caseload/bed managers and ward/floor/community coordinators to gain a global perspective of leadership and management in your area. Discuss challenging communication issues you have experienced with local managers/educators and access available training to support your development, e.g. conflict resolution, de-escalation training and assertiveness study days. Attend leadership and managerial post-registration courses to manage organisational change in the future.

6. Look out for signs of stress in yourself and others. Increase your awareness of 'stress triggers' and identify strategies to prevent and manage stress at work. Always prioritise your physical and mental wellbeing and access professional support if needed.

## REFERENCES AND FURTHER READING

Ablett, J.R. (2007) Resilience and well-being in palliative care staff: a qualitative study of hospice nurses' experience of work. *Psycho-Oncology*, **16**(8): 733–740.

BBC News (2019) *NHS vacancies a 'national emergency'* (online). Available at: www.bbc.co.uk/news/health-45485814 [accessed 12 December 2019]

Bright, J. (1997) *Turning the Tide*. Demos Publishing.

Buchan, J. *et al.* (2019) *A Critical Moment: NHS staffing trends, retention and attrition*. The Health Foundation. Available at: www.health.org.uk/sites/default/files/upload/publications/2019/A%20Critical%20Moment_1.pdf [accessed 12 December 2019]

Bulman, C. and Schutz, S. (2008) *Reflective Practice in Nursing*, 4th edition. Blackwell Publishing.

Burke, A. (2019) Utilizing the Five Rights of Delegation. Available at: www.registerednursing.org/nclex/assignment-delegation-supervision#utilizing-five-rights-delegation [accessed 2 January 2020]

Burton, C.M. and King, L.A. (2004) The health benefits of writing about intensely positive experiences. *Journal of Research in Personality*, **28**: 150–163.

Chinn, T. (2018) Please don't call me 'resilient'. *Nursing in Practice* (online). Available at: www.nursinginpractice.com/please-dont-call-me-resilient [accessed 12 December 2019]

Emmons, R. and McCullough, M. (2003) Counting blessings versus burdens: an experimental investigation of gratitude and subjective well-being in daily life. *Journal of Personality and Social Psychology*, **84(2)**: 377–389.

Floyd, A.C. *et al.* (2007) Affectionate writing reduces total cholesterol: two randomized controlled trials. *Human Communication Research*, **33**: 119–142.

Forde-Johnston, C. (2018) *How to Thrive as a Newly Qualified Nurse*. Lantern Publishing.

Freudenberger, H.J. (1974) Staff burnout. *Journal of Social Issues*, **30**: 159–65.

Gibbs, G. (1988) *Learning by Doing: a guide to teaching and learning methods*. Further Education Unit. Oxford Polytechnic.

Giordano, B. (1997) Resilience: a survival tool for the nineties. *Association of Perioperative Registered Nurses Journal*, **65**: 1032–1036.

Health and Safety Executive (2018) *Work Related Stress, Depression or Anxiety*. London: Crown Copyright.

Health Education England (2018) *Reducing Pre-registration Attrition and Improving Retention*. HEE. Available at: www.hee.nhs.uk/our-work/reducing-pre-registration-attrition-improving-retention [accessed 12 December 2019]

Health Foundation, King's Fund and Nuffield Trust (2019) *Closing the Gap: key areas for action on the health and care workforce*. Available at: www.kingsfund.org.uk/sites/default/files/2019-03/closing-the-gap-health-care-workforce-overview_0.pdf [accessed 12 December 2019]

House of Commons Health Committee (2018) *The Nursing Workforce: second report of session 2017–19*. Available at: https://publications.parliament.uk/pa/cm201719/cmselect/cmhealth/353/353.pdf [accessed 12 December 2019]

Jackson, D., Firtko, A. and Edenborough, M. (2007) Personal resilience as a strategy for surviving and thriving in the face of workplace adversity: a literature review. *Journal of Advanced Nursing*, 60(1): 1–9.

Johns, C. (1995) Framing learning through reflection within Carper's fundamental ways of knowing in nursing. *Journal of Advanced Nursing*, 22: 226–234.

King, L.A. (2001) The health benefits of writing about life goals. *Personality and Social Psychology Bulletin*, 27: 798–807.

King's Fund (2019) *The King's Fund Responds to the Interim NHS People Plan* (online). Available at: www.kingsfund.org.uk/press/press-releases/interim-nhs-people-plan [accessed 12 December 2019]

Lee, R.T. and Ashforth, B.E. (1990) On the meaning of Maslach's three dimensions of burnout. *Journal of Applied Psychology*, 75: 743–747.

Maslach, C. and Leiter, M.P. (2016) Understanding the burnout experience: recent research and its implications for psychiatry. *World Psychiatry*, 15(2): 103–111.

McGowan, J.E. and Murray, K. (2016) Exploring resilience in nursing and midwifery students: a literature review. *Journal of Advanced Nursing*, 72(10): 2272–2283.

McVikar, A. (2003) Workplace stress in nursing: a literature review. *Journal of Advanced Nursing*, 44(6): 635–642.

Mental Health Foundation (2019) *Mental health statistics: mental health at work* (online). Available at: www.mentalhealth.org.uk/statistics/mental-health-statistics-mental-health-work [accessed 12 December 2019]

Francis, R. (2013) *Report of the Mid Staffordshire NHS Foundation Trust Public Inquiry*. The Stationery Office.

Mind (2019) *Less than half of staff think managers would spot their mental health problems, despite two in three managers feeling confident promoting wellbeing* (online). Available at: www.mind.org.uk/news-campaigns/news/less-than-half-of-staff-think-managers-would-spot-their-mental-health-problems-despite-two-in-three-managers-feeling-confident-promoting-wellbeing/ [accessed 12 December 2019]

NHS Digital (2019) *Nurses & Health Visitors absence rates AH2728* (online). Available at: https://digital.nhs.uk/data-and-information/find-data-and-publications/supplementary-information/2019-supplementary-information-files/nurses--health-visitors-absence-rates-ah2728 [accessed 12 December 2019]

NHS England (2019a) *The NHS Long Term Plan.* Available at: www.longtermplan.nhs.uk/wp-content/uploads/2019/08/nhs-long-term-plan-version-1.2.pdf [accessed 12 December 2019]

NHS England (2019b) *Workforce Health and Wellbeing Framework.* Available at: www.nhsemployers.org/-/media/Employers/Publications/Health-and-wellbeing/NHS-Workforce-HWB-Framework_updated-July-18.pdf [accessed 12 December 2019]

NHS England and NHS Improvement (2019) *Interim NHS People Plan.* Available at: www.longtermplan.nhs.uk/wp-content/uploads/2019/05/Interim-NHS-People-Plan_June2019.pdf [accessed 12 December 2019]

NHS Improvement (2019) *Quarterly Performance of the NHS Provider Sector: quarter 4 2018/19* (online). Available at: https://improvement.nhs.uk/resources/quarterly-performance-nhs-provider-sector-quarter-4-201819 [accessed 12 December 2019]

Nursing and Midwifery Council (2017) *The NMC Register: 30 September 2017.* NMC. Available at: www.nmc.org.uk/globalassets/sitedocuments/other-publications/the-nmc-register-30-september-2017.pdf [accessed 2 January 2020]

Nursing and Midwifery Council (2019a) *The NMC Register: 31 March 2019.* NMC. Available at: www.nmc.org.uk/globalassets/sitedocuments/other-publications/nmc-register-data-march-19.pdf [accessed 12 December 2019]

Nursing and Midwifery Council (2019b) *Health and Care Leaders Mark 1,000th Nursing Associate Milestone* (online). NMC. Available at: www.nmc.org.uk/news/press-releases/health-and-care-leaders-mark-1000th-nursing-associate-milestone/ [accessed 12 December 2019]

Oelofsen, N. (2012) *Developing Reflective Practice: a guide for students and practitioners of health and social care.* Lantern Publishing.

Royal College of Nursing (2015) *Stress and You: a guide for nursing staff.* RCN. Available at: www.rcn.org.uk/professional-development/publications/pub-004967 [accessed 12 December 2019]

Royal College of Nursing (2019a) *Bullying and Harassment.* RCN. Available at: www.rcn.org.uk/get-help/rcn-advice/bullying-and-harassment [accessed 12 December 2019]

Royal College of Nursing (2019b) *Join our campaign for safe staffing: the UK picture* (online). RCN. Available at: www.rcn.org.uk/employment-and-pay/safe-staffing [accessed 12 December 2019]

Royal College of Nursing (2019c) *Nursing Degree Application Numbers Still at Crisis Point after Bursary Removal* (online). RCN. Available at: www.rcn.org.uk/news-and-events/news/uk-nursing-degree-ucas-application-numbers-crisis-100719 [accessed 12 December 2019]

Rowe, M. and Sherlock, H. (2005) Stress and verbal abuse in nursing: do burned out nurses eat their young? *Journal of Nursing Management,* **13**(3): 242–248.

Social Partnership Forum (2016) *Tackling Bullying in the NHS: a collective call to action.*

Spera, S. *et al.* (1994) Expressive writing and coping with job loss. *Academy of Management Journal,* **3**: 722–733.

Thomas, L.J. and Revell, S.H. (2016) Resilience in nursing students: an integrative review. *Nurse Education Today,* **36**: 457–462.

Zech, E. (1999) Is it really helpful to verbalize one's emotions? *Gedraf en Gezondheid,* **27**: 42–47.

Zech, E. and Rimé, B. (2005) Is talking about an emotional experience helpful? Effects on emotional recovery and perceived benefits. *Clinical Psychology and Psychotherapy,* **12**: 270–287.

Zerwekh, J. *et al.* (1997) *Concepts of Nursing. Basic care memory notebook of nursing.* Nurse Education Council.

# STEP 7

# MAKE YOUR ACHIEVEMENTS
# STAND OUT IN THE FUTURE

*"Neither look forward where there is doubt nor backward where there is regret. Look inward and ask not if there is anything outside you want, but whether there is anything inside that you have not yet unpacked."*
Quentin Crisp (1908–1999), English writer,
raconteur and actor

## 7.1 SHARE WHAT YOU DO AND PROMOTE YOUR ACHIEVEMENTS

Although this chapter is the shortest, the notion of sharing what you do and making your achievements stand out in the future is important as you move across specialist fields, navigate career pathways or apply for competitive places on post-registration courses. Many newly registered nurses I meet are not thinking about moving up a career ladder when they first qualify and do not feel the need to stand out. Understandably, they are focused on consolidating their knowledge and skills during their first year qualified. However, few remain at band 5 for the duration of their career and within two or three years, they are planning to apply for a band 6 post or a post-registration course.

To give yourself the best opportunity to compete for future posts and post-registration courses, it is important that you focus on promoting your achievements and standing out throughout your career, a premise which underpins every chapter in this book. *Steps 1, 2* and *6* highlight structures to guide your professional development, education and support, to unlock your potential. *Step 3* invites you to consider how you can positively support others and influence change in your current role, to make your application, personal portfolio and CV stand out. *Step 4* presents guidance to complete a strong stand-out application and personal statement, and *Step 5* supports the use of an interview plan to stand out during interviews.

*Step 7* is the culmination of previous steps and focuses on your ability to promote what you do to stand out, asking yourself, as Quentin Crisp states: *"whether there is anything inside that you have not yet unpacked."*

You may stand out by going the extra mile for a patient, colleague or manager, or by providing exemplary team support. There are many local and national awards where individuals are nominated for their compassionate and supportive approach. However, you do not need to amass awards to stand out in practice, as passion, enthusiasm and commitment in a specialist area will shine through. You may have managed a change in practice or overcome barriers and challenges that can be highlighted to others. Within *Step 3*, specific case examples and guidance are presented to help you stand out as you influence change in your role, such as:

- taking a new idea/initiative forward
- joining a national campaign
- becoming a contributor and joining a working party
- leading a service improvement audit/evaluation
- becoming research-active to inform professional knowledge
- disseminating data through publications
- connecting with others and embracing social media
- acting as a role model, and teaching and supporting others
- sharing ideas, resources and experiences with others.

See case examples and guidance relating to each of the above areas in *Section 3.2.1*.

### 7.1.1  *Start small and inspire others*

Promoting excellent practice, creating and contributing to new initiatives, and influencing change using the methods mentioned above, are great ways of standing out and making a difference in your role. It is helpful to others when you highlight the projects you are working on and it is also important to disseminate your findings through networking and publications. Journal editors and professional forums will be interested in your opinions, experiences and insights, as they are valuable to peers who may encounter similar situations in practice. Promoting your achievements helps to support your future career development and inspire colleagues to conduct similar project work.

We have many pockets of good practice across the UK, but not everyone chooses to share their work and experiences. Nurses and midwives may work in silos and feel under-confident sharing their achievements with colleagues. When I encourage staff to share their project work and findings they sometimes say: *"I haven't had time to think about it"*; or they feel their work is not academic enough and their project too small: *"it's just a small local project that no one else will want to know about; it's not a research study"*; or they are put off publishing: *"I wouldn't know where to start with publishing, as I struggled to write essays on my course. No journal will accept my writing."* Try to remember that many individuals start small; for example, you may help out with a local service improvement project before leading a project yourself, or undertake a research internship before developing a clinical academic research career. If you find it difficult to meet the writing standard in a journal, you may write a small piece of narrative in a local newsletter before publishing in a peer-reviewed journal or publish a collaborative paper with other authors.

 **KEY TIP**

- Colleagues are inspired to conduct future projects when they see that their peers have completed simple, feasible and realistic projects. So share your achievements, however small, and inspire others!

### 7.1.2 What? So what? Now what?

Following the completion of any work project, it is helpful to consider the three simple questions below from Rolfe *et al.*'s (2001) reflective model: 'What?', 'So what?' and 'Now what?'

#### What?

- How would you describe your project?
- What type of project work have you undertaken? (see *Section 3.2.1* for details of various types of projects and case examples).

#### So what?

- Who benefits most from your work?
- What do the findings from your project mean for individuals or groups, and/or the specialist field or your profession?
- Who would be most interested in your project experiences and findings?
- How does this project fit within a local/national context?
- How does this project inform the current evidence base?

## Now what?

- Is your project appropriate to share with others? (see *Section 3.3.1*)
- How can your project be promoted and shared with others?
- How are your experiences and findings best disseminated? (*Table 7.1* provides questions and tips to help you promote your project and disseminate findings locally and nationally).

*Table 7.1: Questions and tips to help you promote project work and disseminate findings*

| Questions | Key tips |
|---|---|
| Have you shared your work with your manager? | • **Discuss initiatives and project plans with your line manager and always seek their authorisation and consent, prior to undertaking projects or disseminating your findings** (see *Section 3.3.1*). Health service research studies must follow national consent procedures devised by the UK HRA (see *Section 3.3.2*).<br>• Managers use a variety of ways to communicate with staff, e.g. walk rounds, weekly/monthly staff meetings, posters, newsletters and email. Establish which forum is best to communicate information between you.<br>• Share experiences with your manager as your project evolves and keep them updated with progress. Managers network with key leads who may offer guidance and help promote your work for you as your project progresses.<br>• Ensure that you register project work in your PDR and appraisal documentation (see *Sections 2.4* and *2.5*). |
| Can you share your work across the local Trust/community or university setting? | • **Prior to networking and sharing local project work you should always gain authorisation from your local manager.**<br>• Employers and universities communicate with staff using open staff forums with local leads; corporate walk rounds; global emails; local intranet notices and newsletters.<br>• Network with local leads and offer to act as a link nurse for a specialist area, if relevant to your project.<br>• Join a local working group to implement a service improvement project or to inform local policies, standards, recommendations and regulations.<br>• Use local professional forums to advertise project information across sites, e.g. present at a clinical governance meeting or patient/staff/student group or senior nurse/midwifery meeting.<br>• Register regular project updates in local meeting minutes and newsletters.<br>• Use virtual learning environments and online media communication systems to share good practice, e.g. local Twitter groups and professional forums. Review the NMC (2015) *Guidance on Using Social Media Responsibly* prior to using social media.<br>• Contribute to local staff teaching sessions/study days and supervise others to share your knowledge.<br>• Create health promotional or teaching resources/visuals to share and disseminate local information.<br>• Network with research leads to support the implementation of research/service improvement projects. |

*Table 7.1: (continued)*

| Questions | Key tips |
|---|---|
| Can you share your work nationally? | • **Prior to networking and sharing any local project work nationally, you should always gain authorisation from your manager and chief nurse/midwife.**<br>• Network with national specialist leads, associations and charities to share your experiences and knowledge with others. Through networking you may be able to apply for funding to support future initiatives and research (see *Section 7.2.6*).<br>• Join national working groups and forums, such as RCN professional forums, to nationally benchmark your projects and inform national policies, standards and recommendations.<br>• Register with ORCHID, a system which provides you with a unique digital identifier whilst you undertake research. ORCHID records your professional information and ensures your research is recognised nationally.<br>• Use online media communication systems to engage with national professional Twitter groups to promote and share good practice (see examples of national Twitter groups in *Section 6.1.3*).<br>• Run an online blog or create videos to share your experiences that can be uploaded to YouTube, Facebook and Twitter sites. Adhere to NMC (2015) *Guidance on Using Social Media Responsibly* and the NMC (2018) *Code*, ensuring privacy and confidentiality are maintained prior to posting data online.<br>• Develop critical research skills through post-registration courses to become more 'research-active', and network with national institutions of health research to develop a clinical academic research career (see *Section 7.2*).<br>• Publish your work in a national journal or present at national conferences/study days (see *Section 7.3*).<br>• **When publishing or uploading any material on public sites from your local workplace, you must obtain official authorisation and sign-off from your employer's media and communications department.** Media teams are responsible for managing all internal and external communications and will ensure that the work disseminated meets corporate communication standards, e.g. the correct corporate logo is used (see *Section 3.3.4*). |

The following sections in this chapter focus on two notable ways to help you stand out in your clinical role:
• Develop a clinical academic career
• Publish your work.

Practical tips and advice are offered to help you develop academic, research and publishing skills in the future.

## 7.2 DEVELOP A CLINICAL ACADEMIC CAREER

### 7.2.1 *What is a clinical academic career pathway?*

Westwood and Richardson (2014) provide an excellent visual for a *Clinical Academic Careers Pathway Capability Framework for Nurses, Midwives and Allied Health Professionals*. The framework clearly defines clinical and research capabilities and responsibilities at early, mid and senior career for the Association of UK University Hospitals (AUKUH). Several responsibilities from this clinical academic career pathway are summarised below:

- A person at **early career** stage: assesses, plans, implements and evaluates clinical care for patients/clients and supports research projects in their own specialist area.
- A person at **mid-career** stage: leads changes in practice using specialist expertise, identifies and develops research programmes relevant to practice and is co-investigator on grant applications.
- A person at **senior career** stage: provides clinical and professional leadership in a specialist area across an HEI and NHS organisation, leads the organisational identification of research priorities, and leads research programmes at national/international level.

(adapted from Westwood and Richardson (2014))

The National Institute of Health Research (NIHR) provides excellent advice on building a research career on its website, to guide aspiring clinical researchers (NIHR, 2019). NIHR manages several **Integrated Clinical Academic (ICA) Programmes** that are currently funded by HEE. The **HEE/NIHR ICA Programme** offers opportunities at all levels of a clinical academic career pathway, such as:

- **Internships:** offer clinicians with no prior research experience an introduction to different aspects of clinical research; for example, they may assist on a local research project for a year.
- **Master's studentships:** offer a foundation in clinical research and enable clinicians to obtain a master's.
- **Pre-doctoral clinical fellowships:** allow clinicians to undertake master's-level academic training and prepare an application for a doctorate.
- **Clinical doctoral research fellowships:** enable graduate clinical academics with some research experience to obtain a PhD whilst extending their clinical skills.
- **Clinical lectureship:** enable post-doctorate clinicians to combine independent research in an academic position with continued professional development.

### 7.2.2 What is a clinical academic post?

A clinical academic post allows a healthcare professional to combine working in clinical practice with undertaking academic study and research. Clinical academic posts will have a research or leadership focus, e.g. you link a research study or service improvement evaluation to a leadership course; master's; PhD or post-doctoral programme.

Registered healthcare professionals must formally apply for a clinical academic post that will include the level of the training programme/ university course being offered. Clinical academic posts are usually advertised as clinical **internships, studentships, fellowships** or **lectureships**.

A clinical academic researcher aims to advance practice and transform care whilst having clinical and research responsibilities within a service (Westwood *et al.*, 2013; Westwood and Richardson, 2014).

### 7.2.3 How are you employed in a clinical academic post?

The post-holder is employed by an NHS employer on an agreed pay scale, whilst being registered as a part-time student on a university course. Therefore, the post-holder is paid a wage and their course fees are usually funded for the duration of the course.

The opportunity to study whilst being paid means that clinical academic posts are highly sought-after and extremely competitive; for example, only six posts may be offered across an NHS Trust and hundreds of staff may apply, with only ten being shortlisted.

Clinical academic posts usually have a defined percentage of part-time hours that are split between clinical practice and academic study, e.g. a clinical doctoral research fellowship (CDRF) post may be set up as follows:

- NHS fixed-term contract over 4–5 years
- 0.4 whole time equivalent (WTE) hours undertaking clinical practice = 2 × 8-hour clinical practice days a week
- 0.6 WTE undertaking PhD academic study = 3 × 8-hour days undertaking academic study a week.

### 7.2.4 How do you apply for a clinical academic development opportunity?

Clinical academic internship/studentship/fellowship/lectureship adverts may be open annually/ bi-annually or more regularly, depending on which institution is offering them.

Contact your local and/or regional health service research lead to review what adverts and training opportunities are available locally, regionally and nationally. Most NHS Trusts have a research department and lead for clinical research to offer advice.

Employers will also advertise clinical academic posts and training opportunities on their learning and development intranet sites. Contact corporate education leads for further information about local opportunities. You may have just missed an application deadline and they will know if future opportunities will be coming up again.

Review the NIHR website (www.nihr.ac.uk) where national academic clinical internships, fellowships and lectureships are regularly advertised. Places on HEE/NIHR training programmes are very competitive and applications are open at varying times throughout the year. NIHR clinical academic training programme applications are complex and clear advice is offered for applicants in relation to each programme on their website.

Shortlisting criteria for clinical academic development opportunities will vary according to different providers, but usually require at least six months to one year post-registration experience. Aim to align your research project to the goals of the organisation, and clearly outline how service improvements can be informed by your research.

Prior to submitting an application, thoroughly review the application guidance and never be tempted to submit documents with missing information, as you risk automatic rejection at the shortlisting stage. Applications usually require signed support from a local research supervisor and lead clinical manager.

 **KEY TIP**

- It is important to network with university and Trust research leads well in advance when working up applications.

You must thoroughly understand the research area you wish to study and the programme you will be completing. At master's/PhD level, you are usually required to submit a research proposal as part of your application, which can take up to a year to prepare. Application forms are meticulously peer-reviewed and just being shortlisted is often an achievement in itself (see *Step 4*).

Once shortlisted, an applicant will be called for an interview that adheres to the usual HR checks, and meticulous interview preparation is a must (see *Step 5*).

If your application is unsuccessful, ask for feedback and do not give up, as you can re-apply next time round with a stronger and more informed application.

### 7.2.5  What clinical academic programmes are on offer?

In 2008, the NIHR began offering nationally funded master's and doctorate training schemes to nurses, midwives and allied health professionals. In 2014, HEE launched the Clinical Academic Careers Framework, which restructured the previous Clinical Academic Training Programmes and the Healthcare Science Research Fellowships Programme, extending eligibility criteria to allow more professions to apply. HEE/NIHR clinical academic training programmes currently provide funded opportunities for registered health professionals to gain experience working in a clinical service, whilst undertaking research from internship to post-doctorate level. The chosen area of research must be agreed by NHS partners.

Similarly, clinical academic internships and fellowships have been set up between several UK universities and partner NHS organisations at a variety of levels.

Nottingham University Hospitals (NUH) NHS Trust led the first Chief Nurse Excellence in Care Junior Fellowship to develop the clinical and academic skills of six junior clinical staff. These junior fellows were supported by clinical and academic mentors to complete a service improvement project and bespoke development programme (Bramley *et al.*, 2018). Gloucestershire Hospitals NHS Foundation Trust adapted this NUH programme to provide Chief Nurse Junior Fellowships for "the most talented newly qualified recruits – specifically those with at least a 2:1 degree who have completed the trust's 12-month preceptorship programme" (Jones-Berry, 2019). These fellowships included a Diploma in Leadership and Management.

There is an expectation that more clinical academic opportunities will be offered across the UK in the future. However, there need to be more partnerships between universities and NHS employers to sustain roles and ensure opportunities are more widely available in the future (Westwood *et al.*, 2018).

### 7.2.6  Alternative research funding opportunities

Not everyone is lucky enough to be offered a fully funded clinical academic development opportunity. As an alternative, you may wish to self-fund an academic research programme or apply for external research grants and scholarships. Each grant, bursary or scholarship will state how much is on offer, and provide specific guidance to inform applications on its websites. External funding grants financially support research project costs, and may cover research course fees and/or paid researcher time.

Many charitable organisations provide research funding opportunities open to healthcare professionals. Some websites from institutions that regularly offer opportunities are shown below:

**RCN Scholarships and Bursaries:**
www.rcn.org.uk/professional-development/scholarships-and-bursaries

**The Barbers' Company Clinical Nursing Scholarship:**
https://warwick.ac.uk/fac/sci/med/research/hscience/wrn/nursing scholarship1

**Florence Nightingale Foundation Scholarships:**
https://florence-nightingale-foundation.org.uk/scholarships/

Always contact local research and education leads as well, as there may be some funding offered locally for research studies. Check the local process for applying for future courses (see *Section 2.2.4*).

## 7.3 PUBLISH YOUR WORK

Although we have more educated nurses and midwives with degrees and master's within our profession than ever before, only a small proportion end up publishing their work. Publications are good to have on your CV and personal statement when you apply for jobs or courses, as they make you stand out and demonstrate your motivation and passion for a specialist area.

When I encourage staff or students to publish, they often think that they cannot meet the writing standard required or that their project is not interesting enough. Remember, published work does not always have to be an in-depth research study or systematic review. Just sharing your experiences in an opinion piece can be of interest to others. If you feel nervous about publishing your work, then start small: I began publishing with a simple letter in the *Nursing Times* (Kirrane, 1993). If you have something you are passionate about, try writing it up, as your voice is just as valuable as anyone else's!

I offer workshops to staff and students, to encourage them to publish, and have presented a few tips below to motivate and guide you:

### 7.3.1 *Start with an area you are passionate about and interested in*

- Could you write up a recent literature review or summarise recommendations from a previous assignment?

- Could you share or compare personal experiences, e.g. the transition from being a student to your first post or from an experienced staff nurse to a manager?
- Could you write up your experiences supporting a group of staff or patients/clients?
- Could you comment on national changes in healthcare or reconfiguration of services?
- Are you interested in piloting something new in practice, which could be written up as a service improvement project or an evaluative audit?
- Have you conducted a research study where your findings can be disseminated?

### 7.3.2 Choose the right journal or medium for your publication

- Find out if local communication departments are interested in sharing and publishing your project work.
- National journals have a variety of styles, as they have different target audiences.
- Establish which journals best suit your style by reading a selection of articles from a number of journals.
- You may prefer to disseminate your ideas and narrative on self-publishing blogs and use online visual media.

### 7.3.3 Download authors' guides

Every journal will have an 'Author guide' and it is very important that you download this guide from the journal website, prior to writing your article.
- Always adhere to authors' guidance, which will confirm maximum word limits, along with key article headings for different types of articles, e.g. systematic literatures, service evaluations/audits, research studies and opinion pieces. Always adhere to the word limit, correct headings, font size and referencing style requested, otherwise you risk rejection.
- Always proofread prior to submitting an article. An editor reads thousands of papers and will not spend time correcting your work. Many papers are rejected at an early stage, due to a lack of proofreading and adherence to journal guidance.

### 7.3.4 Contact editors

If you are unsure which journal to choose, you may contact editors about your topic area before you write or send an article for review. This will enable you to find out whether or not they are actually interested in a topic. If they have recently covered a specialist topic area, they may be reluctant to publish a similar article, but you may be able to focus on a different slant within your paper or submit to another journal.

A quick email or phone call will establish whether an editor is interested and this means that you are not left waiting, unable to resubmit to other journals. Once you submit a paper for review it can take several weeks for a response. It is important to note that during this time **it is unethical to submit your paper elsewhere**, which is why it is helpful to have an idea of whether or not the editor is interested.

### 7.3.5 *Start simple and use headings*

- Start off with a smaller piece of writing, e.g. write a letter, case study or reflective piece.
- Start an article, or chapter, with key headings from the authors' guide first. It is much easier to motivate yourself to write, and less daunting, when you are faced with writing under each section.
- Try to avoid procrastinating (see *Table 3.1*).

### 7.3.6 *Seek support and attend workshops and writing groups*

- Attend writing and publication workshops/study days which are available at local or national level. NHS employers and universities may offer publication study time and/or regular writing workshops, where staff who have already published guide and support others.
- Writing groups help to motivate writers, as time is set aside to write during the event.

### 7.3.7 *Collaborate with a co-author*

- If you find writing for publication especially challenging, try collaborating with a co-author.
- If you have difficulties finding a co-author, ask local universities and local education leads, as they aim to promote publications across all fields.
- When collaborating with others, always ensure you are all clear on the order of authorship prior to writing the article, to avoid disagreements later. Is your surname going to go first on the reference or does the person writing the paper expect to be first?
- The first name in an author list is the most desirable position in a publication. After the first author, successive authors are then listed according to their contribution to the research or writing process.

## ─── WHAT TO DO NEXT ───

1. Make a list of clinical projects you have been involved with. Use the three questions from Rolfe *et al.*'s (2001) reflective model: 'What?', 'So what?' and 'Now what?' to decide how best to share and disseminate project work to make it stand out.

2. Use relevant methods to share and disseminate project findings, e.g. attend staff meetings and join professional forum groups; create videos and newsletters; present data on social media and local intranet sites; deliver staff/patient teaching sessions and supervise others; and publish in national journals. Review the NMC's (2015) *Guidance on Using Social Media Responsibly* prior to using social media.

3. Contact local university healthcare departments to identify collaborative research projects you could support. Discuss your research ideas and proposals with research-active experienced staff. Join local clinical research groups to discuss your area of interest and network with other researchers.

4. Network with the NIHR and local manager, educator and research leads, to develop a clinical academic research career. Contact local and regional health service research leads to review what adverts and training opportunities are available. Look out for future clinical academic posts and training opportunities on local learning and development intranet sites.

5. Review the NIHR website (www.nihr.ac.uk) where national academic clinical internships, fellowships and lectureships are regularly advertised. Review NIHR guidance for applications.

6. Align future research proposals to the goals of the organisation, and clearly outline how service improvements can be informed by your research, to increase your chance of funding on future applications.

7. Apply for external research grants and scholarships to support post-registration courses to become more 'research-active'.

8. Attend local and national publication workshops to develop your writing skills and increase your chance of publishing in the future.

## REFERENCES AND FURTHER READING

Bramley, L. *et al.* (2018) Engaging and developing front-line clinical nurses to drive care excellence: evaluating the Chief Nurse Excellence in Care Junior Fellowship initiative. *Journal of Research in Nursing*, **23**(8): 678–689.

Health Education England (2018) *Clinical Academic Careers Framework: a framework for optimising clinical academic careers across healthcare professions*. Available at: www.hee.nhs.uk/sites/default/files/documents/2018-02%20CAC%20Framework.pdf [accessed 16 December 2019]

Jones-Berry, S. (2019) Scheme to develop nurses' clinical and academic skills improves job satisfaction. *Nursing Standard*, **34**(9): 15.

Kirrane, C. (1993) Informed help wanted on making post-basic education choices. *Nursing Times*, **89**(7): 12.

National Institute for Health Research (2019) *Building a Research Career*. NIHR. Available at: www.nihr.ac.uk/documents/building-a-research-career/20571 [accessed 16 December 2019]

Nursing and Midwifery Council (2015) *Guidance on Using Social Media Responsibly*. NMC. Available at: www.nmc.org.uk/globalassets/sitedocuments/nmc-publications/social-media-guidance.pdf [accessed 16 December 2019]

Nursing and Midwifery Council (2018) *The Code: professional standards of practice and behaviour for nurses, midwives and nursing associates*. NMC. Available at: www.nmc.org.uk/globalassets/sitedocuments/nmc-publications/nmc-code.pdf [accessed 16 December 2019]

Rolfe, G. *et al.* (2001) *Critical Reflection in Nursing and the Helping Professions: a user's guide*. Palgrave Macmillan.

Westwood, G. *et al.* (2013) How clinical academics are transforming patient care. *HSJ*, 28–32 (online). Available at: www.hsj.co.uk/topics/technology-and-innovation/how-clinical-academics-are-transforming-patient-care/5062463.article [accessed 16 December 2019]

Westwood, G. *et al.* (2018) Building clinical academic leadership capacity: sustainability through partnership. *Journal of Research in Nursing*, **23**(4): 346–357.

Westwood, G. and Richardson, A. (2014) *Clinical Academic Careers Pathway Capability Framework for Nurses, Midwives and Allied Health Professionals*. The Association of UK University Hospital. Available at: www.southampton.ac.uk/assets/centresresearch/documents/wphs/AUKUH-Clinical-Academic-Careers-Capability-Framework-May-2014-4.pdf [accessed 16 December 2019]

# INDEX